SHOOT THE WOMEN FIRST

Gripping, topical and gut-wrenching true-life adventure
memoir of British born intelligence agent Andrea Davison

Andrea Davison and Tom Doe

BELLATRIX BOOKS WYOMING

Shoot the Women First

For information contact:

info@bellatrixbooks.com

http://www.bellatrixbooks.com

Book and Cover design by Tom Doe

ISBN: 978-0-9996020-0-3

First Edition: December 2017

WRITTEN IN THE PUBLIC INTEREST

Shoot The Women First is written in the Public Interest and includes public figures whom the author Andrea Davison knew personally. Public figures and the dead do not need their privacy protected. Events, characters names and conversations have been changed to protect the identity of the less well known, the unknown and the secret.

This memoir portrays authentic events in the life of the author as honestly and truthfully as recollection enables or research can verify. The authors extensive records, letters and diaries were seized by Police, acting to protect a criminal element within the British State. The loss of these documents has hindered the authors, causing possible alteration in the timeline of events.

Some events have been tweaked for dramatic and narrative reasons, others compressed, and dialogue reconstructed. Shoot The Women First is a dramatization based on living truth, a reflection of experiences in past times but still vibrant in the authors memory. The authors accept other people may have different memories.

The Official Secrets Act, a law of the United Kingdom of Great Britain and Northern Ireland makes it mandatory for manuscripts written by former professionals from the Special Forces, security, or intelligence services to be submitted for clearance to the Ministry of Defence. Andrea Davison has declined to submit this manuscript to the current ruling elite, who have betrayed so many former agents and good citizens, as well as their own country Great Britain. Instead, the authors rely on the international laws of free speech, Article 10 of the European Convention on Human Rights and the United States First Amendment, which guarantees freedom of expression.

\

Dedicated to all the children and
animals who suffered abuse, but
found love anyway; and to Pluto,
the puppy who grew into a horse
and saved my heart.

CONTENTS

1. BASTARD SON

"One day I'm going to go up in a helicopter and it'll just blow up. MI5 will do away with me." Princess Diana

Tom dashed into the kitchen carrying a bundle of papers, an old leather case and a bottle of Champagne. Shutting the door behind him, he sat down opposite me. Outside the night had drawn a blanket of stars over the Comechingones Mountains. People had lived here since the first moon shone on a home.

"Your Macur Statement is going viral. It's getting the truth out there," Tom said.

"I hope so. The victims are so vulnerable."

"If you have the Serco report, I'll take it with me to BA tomorrow."

Pushing the laptop across the table, I said, "I'm editing, but take a look, and see what you think."

The clock in the corner paced out time, as we read together.

A loud hammering on the door startled us. Our eyes met in a glance of silent communication, Tom's pupils dilated and I read his dark thoughts, *'sounds like police'.*

The hammering resumed, but here in Argentina, I had no reason to fear the Police. Time stood still, frozen in urgency, and then the pounding stopped. Silence hung in the air like the aftermath of a nuclear explosion. Tom sprang up and was at the kitchen door when it flew open and a young man, brandishing a pistol, rushed in. Tom smashed his gun arm against the wall. The gun tumbled from his grasp, as a second armed man rushed in, striking Tom over the head with his handgun.

"We have just come for the documents," he bellowed in perfect English. W*as this statement supposed to calm us?*

My training kicked in like a snort of cocaine; seconds became minutes as I assessed the scene. Tom was on the floor his blood splattering the white walls as he grappled, half concussed, with the first assailant. The second man stood pointing his gun at the duo, now locked like passionate lovers in an embrace. Telepathically Tom said, *'Get the machete; I'll buy you time.'*

Neither assailant noticed me turn and run down the corridor to the bedroom. Thrusting my hand under the pillow, I found the machete Tom had put there earlier. Drawing it out the blade glinted in the cold electric light. That morning, Tom had spent hours sharpening its edge top and bottom. "More frightening than a 9mm close up," he said prophetically.

Narrowing my thoughts to a perfect point, I stroked the blade with a snipers instinct. Brandishing the Machete, I ran down the corridor back to the kitchen. Tom was still struggling and rolling on the floor with the first attacker. The second man, hearing steps turned bringing up his gun level with my face. Subconsciously I noted the matt black metal of the small gun, the trained stance, his youthful, handsome face. Raising the blade in a seamless movement, I angled it to take off his head at the neck. Staring into his hard chocolate eyes for a fraction of a second I grasped the power, he quailed, turned and fled. It was a good choice; his .32 caliber bullets would not have stopped me in the five feet between us.

Tom, sensing it was over relaxed his grip on the first attacker, who snatched up his fallen gun, fleeing after his friend.

"Tom, are you Okay," I asked, as he stood up shaky and dazed, blood streaming from his open wound into his eyes and down his cheeks. Lifting a hand to wipe away the blood, he said,

"Fine; I'm fine. Lock the door."

Twisting the key in the door, I went back to help him.

"Sit down," I said, leading him to a straight-backed wooden chair.

He collapsed into it, as the adrenaline stopped pumping through his veins.

We needed help, so picking up the cell phone I rang Beth, who lived on the high slopes of the mountains overlooking my house.

"Beth its Tara, two gunmen attacked us, please phone the Chief."

"Where are you?"

"At home."

"Wait there, I will come soon."

Our mutual friend, the Chief of Police is a charming and resourceful man. He helped me settle into my new country by finding Beth. She was one of those rare and beautiful people who would do anything for anybody. Her husband Richard spent his working life, creating special effects in films and thrilling people with his magic tricks. Somewhere on his journeys, this Englishman found a dark beauty with the heart of an angel.

In what seemed like only minutes, the Chief had everything locked down and his team of plain-clothed officers was in the house. Tom went in a police car to the local hospital along with Beth as an interpreter. A police officer in dark jumper, combat pants and short black combat boots, sat with me, while the house and garden was dusted for prints.

In Argentina, children learn English at School so even with my poor Spanish I could make myself understood. A detective with a moon face and tough look said, "Get the valuables and go to another casa. Do you have somewhere to go?"

"I have amigos who live nearby, I will phone them."

As the detective watched, I called Alicia and filled her in on the details.

Alicia is of German extraction, married to Cletus a full-blooded German. They made a complimentary couple. Alicia surrounded herself with family and friends, doling out ladles of love. Cletus was the strong man of the duo brave and brusque. Cletus came on the phone, and I repeated the story, when I told him about the Machete, he chuckled.

"We're on holiday right now, but Carl and Otto are there. Just stay at the Cabaña by the pool. Stay as long as you like." Cletus said.

Thirty minutes later, Tom flounced in with Beth. He was battered and sporting a few stitches over his right eye.

"The hospital was excellent. We went right to the top of the queue."

"That's great. Alicia and Cletus are giving us the cute spare house by the pool."

"Fantastic. We need to get you out of here," Tom said.

Beth nodded agreement.

When the detectives finished, Beth drove us to our friend's hacienda, then returned home.

Entering the compound, Otto greeted us with his Pocket Browning. We embraced as the seven-foot tall electric gates closed behind us. The hacienda was under lockdown, surrounded by high fences and paroled by four big dogs who knew us well.

Otto had been a Hitler Youth, but that was long ago. His haggard face, patrician nose and sky blue eyes looked at me with compassion. His command of English and Spanish was like my command of German, almost zero. However, warmth and friendship are a language of their own.

Carl, his grandson, was a strapping lad of seventeen. His close-cropped blond hair adorned refined carved features and a razor-sharp mind. He was the epitome of his German heritage, but the furthest youth from Hitler's conscripts as could be. Carl had inherited his Mother's caring nature and his Father's bravery.

"Come, the Cabaña is ready for you," Carl said, "Dad told me what happened, are you both OK."

"Thanks, we're fine."

Grandfather and grandson, the old tree and the sapling would not let any intruder in alive.

The Cabaña's red clay tiled roof overhung the red brick walls. Rows of bricks interlaced with cosmetic concrete slices reminiscent of the witch's house in Hansel and Gretel made out of sweets. Towels, sheets and pillowcases were stacked up on a bench and the water heater was on.

We dumped everything on the kitchen floor and opened a bottle of Champagne. Grabbing two wine glasses from the cupboard, I went outside.

It had been a hot day and the evening warmth was balmy. A potted jasmine grew by the door its tendrils thick with small white heavily scented flowers. Surrounded by its fragrance, we settled down at the table by the dark and sky blue tiled pool. Two of the dogs nestled close knowing something had happened.

"Well, life is never boring. You did well," I said.

"That's what Staff taught me, in close, go for the gun arm."

We smiled at each other. The danger had passed and finally drained away with the first sip of champagne. We were safe, we were happy and life was full of possibilities.

The cell phone rang, intruding on our peace,

"Hello."

"Are you Okay?" a familiar American voice said.

Ronald was a former arms dealer and a King Saud favorite who had worked along with the agency for donkey's years.

"Yes, just two idiots with guns."

We never listened to each other's calls, so Tom took his glass and returned to the Cabaña.

"We'll send up some people from BA," [1] Ronald said.

"No, it's okay; I have plenty of protection right here, but how…"

"Grapevine. Are you sure you're Okay, we can send someone?"

---

[1] Buenos Aires

The soft head of an Alsatian brushed against my knee.

"No, really, we are safe here, friends are looking after us."

"Who were the men?" Ronald asked.

"I don't know. The men were young, early 20's, one spoke perfect English. He said they just wanted to rob me of the documents."

"Maybe from the HALO program they recruit kids from all over, but this is not authorized through the chain of command, I can tell you that."

"Expect it's the 'nutters' in the UK."

"I will check it out. Hey, how is your report going?"

"Nearly finished," I said as my fingers ruffled the Alsatians fur.

"Maybe they don't appreciate your Macur Statement."[2] He said.

"Maybe not, but it's just a snapshot."

"This campaign has got you into heaps of trouble already. Then you get it published on David Icke's website."

"David is a friend. I'm not giving it up for a couple of punks with guns."

"Well it's a risk, makes you a threat on so many levels. They're capricious, rich, powerful, corrupt and insane."

"You're right, about that,"

" "And then you escaped!"

"Yes."

"They intended to drive you into the ground, stripping you of all hope as injustice after injustice knocked you down."

"Then they forget how resilient old agents can be."

"Look, I will check out who is behind this."

"Hey, thanks for all."

---

[2] The Statement of Andrea Davison to the Macur Review of the Waterhouse judicial Inquiry into child abuse in Children's Homes in North Wales UK. See Appendix.

"My pleasure. You take care."

Putting down the cell phone, I called out,

"Tom."

"Yes."

"That was Ronald asking after us, he offered to send up some guys from BA, but I said we were OK."

Tom appeared through the door, followed by a Belgium Collie. Sitting down, stroking the dog's glossy head, he said, "I phoned Cletus and Alicia. When I described the guy who threatened you, Alicia said it sounded like the bastard son of a British Diplomat. His Mum lives close by and is in with some strange military types, she said."

"That may be just tittle-tattle, it could be some punks from Cordoba and a few thousand pesos can buy a lot here. Ronald says it was unauthorized, so it could indeed be the bastards at the Embassy."

"Bastards indeed," Tom laughed.

Beyond the compound, the Mountains climbed to the starry speckled heavens. An owl shrieked into the calm, as the full moon lent down silver fingers to crest the tiny waves of the pool. Spectral memories of the journey from youth to wisdom splattered like raindrops on the window of my mind.

2. ELEPHANT CAGE

"Fortunately, some are born with spiritual immune systems that sooner or later give rejection to the illusionary worldview grafted upon them from birth through social conditioning. They begin sensing that something is amiss, and start looking for answers. Inner knowledge and anomalous outer experiences show them a side of reality others are oblivious to, and so begins their journey of awakening. Each step of the journey is made by following the heart instead of following the crowd and by choosing knowledge over the veils of ignorance." Henri Bergson

Shaking away sleep, I rose to peer out of the bedroom window. The golden globe of the dawn sun, washed out by spidery web clouds, crested the rolling hills of Dunstable Downs. Framed, before the grassy green and brown slopes, a solitary kite skimmed the air traveling on an updraft.

Shivering in the fresh air, I hurried into some washed-out jeans and a moss green army t-shirt. Then grabbing a worn-out army cap, thrust it on my golden curls and slipped quietly down the stairs.

Opening the front door, the morning light greeted me with a blast of cold air. Goose pimples crawled up my arms, all forgotten in my heady race to the corner of the street.

Just where the emptiness of the downs gave way to rows of houses with flower-filled red, green, gold and blue gardens, the new Station Wagon waited.

"Morning Mam," said the fresh-faced private in the white short-sleeved shirt, his soft Texan drawl washing over me like hot chocolate over ice cream.

The fifteen-mile drive to Chicksands USAF base flashed past in a whirl of green trees and brown earth. Chicksands base was like a country park with a blue river snaking through its green tended lawns. A river where thousands of fish swim unseen, moving their fins rhythmically or hovering under the falling green and silver tendrils of Weeping Willows. Close to the river banks sprawled with unassuming grandeur, a 12th Century Priory in gold and russet stone. On these grounds, nuns in white habits had strolled, prayed and chanted liturgies before King Henry the Eighth evicted them. That was long before the sound of bullets firing began and the 'Elephant cage' appeared. A monstrous, open weave steel cold war listening post in the Iron Horse HF direction finding world network, nicknamed the Elephant Cage.

The Chauffeur delivered me punctiliously to Tony.

"Hello Tara," Tony said.

A short time ago, he had taken up residence at the base for some unknown reason.

"Hello, Tony."

"I hear you're having trouble loading your magazines."

"Yes," I said, "I am slow, all butterfingers."

He stiffened, annoyed at the childlike statement. At eighteen, lithe with long red-gold hair tumbling down in twisted curls, large eyes the color of ocean blue paint in small Greek villages; I knew I was a beauty. Well, everyone said so. Tony, however, was unimpressed.

"To survive you must load your rifle quickly," he said, towering over me, more due to his bulk than his height.

Everything about him spoke parachute regiment. His degree in history and his penchant for Irish history, in particular, gave authenticity to the storyteller he was.

In the past, his training had included how to spot where the rifle fire was coming from, and how to evade capture. He had instructed me to shoot the women first because they will never give up and made me laugh at his repertoire of stories. Now he would teach me how to load the rifle magazines.

"I have no problem with handgun magazines they fit so neatly into the hand, but these rifle magazines are too big. I'm not sure I'll ever need a rifle anyway."

"You need to pick up any asset you find in the field. Let's begin," he said, laying out the bullets in an intimate little group on the table, their copper heads glinting where touched by a ray from the naked light bulb.

"Load."

Picking up the dark gray magazine, I snatched up a bullet from the pile trying to push it into the magazine. It was like shoving a round peg into a square hole. *I would never learn.*

Looking at the floor, I said, "It's just too difficult."

Then the room plunged into darkness. Tony had turned off the lights. *What is he doing?*

"Load," he barked.

Thoughts suddenly drained away. By instinct, I reached for the pile of bullets that now felt so familiar and loaded the magazine with lightning speed. Flicking the light back on, he looked down at me with a question in his eyes.

Meeting his gaze, I said "Wow that was so easy."

"You've been trained, like every soldier, to load in the dark."

"But I don't remember being trained," I said, putting the loaded magazine down, "I don't remember loading magazines before except for handguns."

"You've been trained that's a definite. Now try again."

Passing me a thirty round magazine, with thirty loose bullets he doused the light. I loaded the magazine with total professionalism. Tony was right; I had been trained. Somewhere in my subconscious lay the key to where and how and by whom. Then I was on the other side of the looking glass, propelled there by this stark moment of awareness. The world was not what I believed it to be, not what I had been taught it was, not even remotely fitting the frame, I had been given. The world was entirely different, utterly exciting and scarily dangerous all at the same time. *If I was trained to load magazines in the dark, what else had I been trained to do.*

Only the week before, moments after declaring victory in the California Democratic Primary, Senator Robert Kennedy lay dying of several small bullet wounds. The twenty-four-year-old Palestinian refugee who had fired his eight-round .22 revolver at the Senator said, he remembered nothing about the shooting. It was the buzz with insiders, talking in hushed tones about secret mind control, behavior modification and hypnosis and drug experiments conducted by Nazi officers.

Robert's brother, President John F Kennedy, himself assassinated five years before had made a speech to the American Newspaper Publishers Association. In it, he explained that the enemies of humanity had infiltrated every section of society in a secret war against truth and compassion, in a single evil-minded pursuit of power for a handful of elite mobsters.

Looking down at the thirty round loaded magazine, I thought about the boys in Vietnam, killing and being killed to protect the heroin trade. Robert Kennedy had sent a message of non-violence and unity, by his opposition to racism and conflict:

"We want peace in Vietnam," he had said.

That, of course, was a direct threat to the warmongers and he paid the price with his life.

Like his brother, he was conscious of the dark forces seeking to dominate every aspect of government, running like black oil behind Police, Judiciary, civil offices and political positions:

"If they are going to shoot, they'll shoot," Robert Kennedy told his aide Fred Dutton.

Tony's voice cut through this gloomy reverie,

"Tara don't get lost."

Snapping back to the present, I looked up at him, "Just thinking about Robert Kennedy and wondering what I had been trained to do."

"It's all levels," Tony said.

"Yes, but has my memory been professionally obscured and

why?"

"I'm just here to make sure you survive Tara."

On the way back home, as the station wagon meandered through the clean, green, gold and brown countryside, I searched for a point when the training began, but it was lost in the miasma of forgotten moments. As children, we have a way of filtering experiences into a subjective phenomenon and our survival instinct is as natural as any young animals. Looking at a blank screen in my mind, only the emotions poured through, unremitting in their terror but without form, without cohesion. When the driver dropped me off and drew away, I was glad to be alone; I needed to face some inner demons.

Mother was at work and the house echoed quiet and empty as I walked upstairs to my room. Phantoms from childhood mushroomed around, somewhere buried in my subconscious, memories lay which could unlock the events of today. *Could I be a trained assassin and not know it.* Eerie images fought their way into my consciousness and I could not fight them back.

Five years ago, I had just turned thirteen and was being dragged through Leeds Police Station corridors by my long hair. My body bumped along smashing into the stark gray walls. Thrown into a cell, I sprawled on the cold concrete floor looking up at the metal door where the two officers, in their early thirties, stood one on either side.

Then they were on me again, the man pinning down my child's right hand onto the cell bunk with his big hands while the woman produced a pair of scissors. Searing pain, followed by blood splattering red onto the floor of the cell as she cut my fingernails to the quick. First my right hand and then my left.

The man pulled my dress tearing it off me, as the woman held me down. A hard hand muffled my mouth and I could not breathe or shout.

"Shut up," he said, twisting my hands behind my back and clamping handcuffs onto my wrists.

Naked and handcuffed, they threw me the hard bunk, assaulted me, then left, locking the massive metal door behind them.

Alone, I lay naked, covered in blood, metal handcuffs chafing my skin. An extreme calm enveloped me. I felt nothing, no pain, no sadness, no hatred. I had disassociated from the torture and abuse.

The cry of a seagull outside the bedroom window sent the Phantoms running. Blinking back to the present, I surveyed the surroundings, I was alone and no longer a child. Still fear clung around like a dark cloak as I tried to push back the images of the child I had been, but the memories kept coming.

The State prosecuted the child, for being drunk and disorderly, throwing me headlong into an abusive system of Police, Courts, psychopaths and pedophiles. Torn from my mother's care, branded for life, to be a pawn in their game. They incarcerated me in Duncroft, an Approved School for highly intelligent disturbed girls. The school's visitors included Princess Alexandra and after I left serial pedophile Sir Jimmy Savile. It was a terrible place and one night I absconded by climbing out of a third-floor window by tying sheets together.

From the moment, I walked out through the gates of Duncroft and climbed into the back of a black car the memories stopped.

Tears began to flow; I wept now for the child who could not cry. Drifting into a troubled sleep, I was awoken by mother's footsteps on the stairs.

She knocked on the door,

"Hello,"

"Hello Mama, come in."

A great beauty in her youth at fifty-six her bone structure still lifted her facial skin into a pleasing form, her hair once as gold and blond as mine was now sprinkled with pepper and salt. But her eyes, the color of speedwells gazed out as bright as ever, sparkling with intelligence.

During World War Two, she was the secretary of Mr. Blackwell, who made seaplanes amongst other things. Her generation was coached not to talk, so it was hard to prize even the smallest secret from her. Then without warning alarming and fascinating moments of her life would spill out from her ordered world.

To me, she was the most wonderful warm and loving being. We shared a bond forged through many lives, she told me.

"Dinner is at seven," she said.

"Okay."

That evening, after dinner, as we sat alone together in the lounge, I told her what had happened at Chicksands. Mama and I never spoke about Duncroft or the Police. It was too painful for her. She could not forgive herself.

"Why are these memories hidden behind a veil?" I asked her.

She reached into an antique bureau made of layered walnut veneer; darkest brown spun with golden whorls and pulled out a folder. Laying the crème folder, adorned with Rosicrucian emblems a triangle with a sun and rose, on the coffee table between us. At her knee, I learned to recognize astrological symbols and draw birth charts using an Ephemeris. We would often pore over astrological charts together, engrossed in the fascination of the power of the planets and the way they affected each other and life, as the moon affects the tides.

"No-one knows what hides in their subconscious," she said, pulling out my birth chart from the folder, "but the plan of your life is told in the stars."

Picking up the chart she said, "Venus, Jupiter and Ascendant oppose Pluto in Leo and Neptune conjuncts Mars. Your path is to find a profound balance between your outer and inner life. Self-mastery is achieved by facing all fears thus forging a pathway to enlightenment and deep peace," Putting the chart back on the table, her sharp eyes considered me.

"Pluto is working with you at a deep level so you can heal yourself, face your karma and help humanity heal through compassion. At a deep alchemical level, the plutonian lead must be turned into Plutonian gold. Your path will not be easy, but it will be so very rewarding."

As her words ebbed from her knowledge, they seeped into my soul and I saw my path through her eyes. She was looking into a future I could yet only glimpse, but saw as if by osmosis through her sight.

"As an agent, you will deal in the world of illusion on every level," she said, tracing the astrological symbols with her fingers. "Confronted with deception, you must divest yourself of delusion and hone the powers of your consciousness, to create an alternate controllable illusion. You should aim to become like the fool in the tarot deck, finely balancing the forces of the universe." she looked upwards as if she did not see the white painted ceiling, but some vast cosmos of stars.

"Free will is the law of attraction. It's all about energy," she said, moving her hands in a wide arc, manifesting some hidden power through her movements. "The energy of electricity, the energy inside an atom, the energy of thoughts, feeling, perception and consciousness. This illusion is all about energy."

"Yes, I see, but I am human and I have a body."

Being human is a perception, honed in the early years when the view between worlds is still thin and the possibilities are endless. Power is by its nature free and the will which drives it is also free."

The room had grown dark, outside the setting sun cast a soft blue light through the open windows. Then in a moment, the light had gone and the room melted into the shadows. We were mother and daughter in an intimacy of thought and experience like the priestesses of some forgotten land. The drapes a moment before a satin display of bright colored flowers became basalt and marble columns as the fingers of night etched a new world out of this very ordinary room. Through the darkness, her clear voice with a vibrant edge rang into the shadows.

"If you give your power to another person or a government or leader then you are feeding them. Be careful in whom you believe and to whom you give the sacred power of your will too. Be careful also which philosophy or belief, you transfix with power."

"I will take care not to get lost."

"You are young and must learn to be sharply aware, must feel if eyes are watching, must know what is coming up ahead."

Fixing me with a soul-searing stare, she said, "This is a dangerous and serious game. It is a battle between dragons."

"But what am I being trained for," I asked, aware my questions had not been answered and the memories still lay dark and hidden without explanation.

"You either know the answer to that, or it is not the time."

She was speaking in riddles, *would I ever understand.*

3 . PETALS OF DEATH

"I don't think people realize how the establishment became established. It simply stole the land and property off the poor, surrounded themselves with weak minded sycophants for protection, gave themselves titles and have been wielding power ever since." Tony Benn MP

The hotel was a monumental old raj building. It sprawled like a giant white bird with a central head and two outstretched sheltering wings. The rooms had high vaulted ceilings dotted with whirling fans, which emitted a swish, swish sound as they twirled in the heat-laden air.

Littered here and there were narrow corridors and stairs with servants rushing up and down. In India, people were legion; poverty stalked the land, so servants were cheap and bountiful. Jai was the servant assigned to me, he was middle-aged, dressed in simple flowing white robes, which covered him from top to toe, all tied up with a thick ornamental rope. This ensemble passed as a hotel uniform. Jai ran errands for me and brought me what I needed, always making sure I had fresh drinking water, soap, clean towels.

Jai and I had formed a bond since the time he rushed to me disheveled, distraught and afraid. Trembling from head to foot, he blurted out

"Madam, madam, the Germans have thrown me down the stairs."

"Sit down Jai"

"No Madam, I dare not," he said, struggling to remain upright.

"Okay, go and get me some fresh water and take a long time over it, I will go and see the Germans."

Rising from the rattan seat, I smoothed out the silk ruffles of my cream dress and picked up my handbag. A Walther PK nestled next to my lipstick and hairbrush. I slung the golden snakeskin bag over my shoulder on its slender double straps. Watching Jai hobble off towards the kitchens, I climbed the stairs to the Germans room and knocked.

Framed in the open doorway two blond, blue-eyed giants below thirty stared out at me, their arrogant disposition impossible to conceal.

"Good Morning Gentlemen, my servant tells me you have assaulted him. With respect may I warn you that it would not be to your advantage to molest Jai again."

They looked at me blankly.

"Do you understand?" I asked, "Should I acquire an interpreter?"

"No," the biggest one said his hand still resting on the open door, "I understand English, that Indian is an idiot."

"That Indian, Gentlemen, is my servant and it may be he does not understand your accent. If you have any difficulty communicating with him I am on the bottom floor by the fountain and I will be happy to interpret."

Jai and I had been firm friends from that day, I trusted him to run errands, he passed me information about the guests and I tipped him generously.

Today he brought a note, sealed in a rough blank paper envelope. Tearing it open, I read, 'I am in Delhi so have sent Zaid to pick you up on a Harley. Will you please come with him. I await you with cake and tea. I am not alone, bring your passport. Best Aarif.'

Jai stood waiting patiently by the door as I finished reading,

"Please tell the gentleman, I will be ten minutes."

He nodded with that strange, twisted side-to-side nod which

meant yes in India, but no everywhere else in the world.

Disappearing into the room, I flung open the wardrobe door to inspect the poor collection of traveler's clothes within. It was a hot day, so the Englishwoman in Africa look would suit. Grabbing a pair of fatigue pants in desert gold, I pulled the silk dress over my head flinging it on the bed. The pants were light and soft with pockets on the legs, a short-sleeved light matching cotton shirt with button-down pockets and a button-down collar completed the look. Too warm to wear boots I chose a simple pair of soft brown loafers with thick heels to give me a little height. Pulling out a small knapsack from under the bed, I emptied the contents of my handbag into it. With the application of a little rose pink lipstick for that innocent look, I was outside of the door and turning the Key.

Jai hovered on the other side of the massive Courtyard in case I needed him. Walking through the oversized wrought iron entrance gates, I spotted Zaid. He sat relaxed on the Harley, one foot on the pavement for balance. The vast bulk of the motorbike seemed too big for his slender form, but he was a fighting man rippling with muscles.

Except for the people shuffling in and out of the large houses and the occasional car drifting past, the broad avenue was quiet. This part of Delhi had been the center of a long-dead Raj. Here the British had flaunted their wealth amidst the suffering masses of a country they had stolen, until Mahatma Gandhi, dressed in a loincloth, by fasting had won back India.

Walking the few paces to Zaid, the pulse and magical heart of India touched me. As I approached, he stiffened; there was no point in greeting him, as during the years I had known him he had not once spoken to me.

Placing my left foot on the rear footrest, I propelled myself into the air, landing squarely on the back seat with a comforting plump. Once aboard Zaid moved forward. Either he was forbidden to touch me, or he did not want to. He engaged gear, tearing through the air like a bolt out of a crossbow. Grabbing the metal brace behind me, I relaxed into a motionless stance, letting him take me I knew not where.

At the corners, we tipped at a sharp angle to the ground then returned upright. Buildings, then tenements flashed by in a whirl of color. Closing my eyes to keep out the grit, I experienced the amazing race through space. The bumps on the road, tilting round corners, flashes of sun and dappled shadows across my inner lids as the bike sped on.

Then the pace slackened, opening my eyes I saw two enormous black iron gates, set in a high biscuit and red colored wall. As we approached, the right-hand gate swung open and we thundered past down a short drive to stop at the main door. The entrance towered ten feet high and opened onto a courtyard tiled in gold, ochre and red. Graceful verandas sat on top of elegant Greco–roman pillars of russet stone. A gust of wind set hanging mirrored fabric billowing. The sun caught the mirrors casting iridescent sparkles on the tiles.

Through the courtyard, Aarif walked towards me. We embraced in the way family do, a quiet, non-hug.

"Tara, please come in," he said, in his cultured English.

He led me through a room, where twelve rough men in ethnic dress sat at a table silenced by my entry. They would never invite me to sit with them. Aarif did not introduce me, he was an Afghan warlord and they would do what he told them.

Leading me through another room with a high vaulted ceiling, we entered into the gardens. On the terrace, a bamboo table with six chairs sprawled, surrounded by tropical plants in blues and reds tumbling from giant ochre colored pots. The pots had lips edged in gold, with a blue painted flower motif etched with skill into the center. Surrounding the terrace, climbing jasmine hung laden with white flowers. The petals fell onto the ochre tiled floors and hid under the tables and chairs. My shoes crushed the white blooms releasing a heady perfume.

"It's beautiful Aarif."

"Yes, it is," he agreed, pointing to a bamboo chair cushioned in gold and red.

The soft cushion gave way under me as I sank into it.

"When did you leave Goa?" I asked him, as he took a seat opposite.

"Last week. I'm organizing the movement of powder."

He was talking about Heroin. The Mujahedeen were the world's biggest Heroin traffickers. They traded heroin for arms mainly with the CIA, MI6 and their networks of front companies.

"We have problems, you know the men are forbidden to take the powder, but too many good guys are, it's the nature of the business."

"I've heard. You would think they'd know not to touch the stuff. It's hurting India, your powder is too pure and it's more addictive than the cut products in the West."

"We don't cut the powder," he said, "we leave that for the customers to do, it's a dirty business. But let's talk about other things Tara; we have only a little time."

Our friendship was born of kinship. An enigmatic, ineffable mystical quality, which bonded our race together. Aarif's ancestors like mine, the Berbers, and the Basques were from the same ancient blood.

"The old wisdom is retreating. Wherever the Old Testament religions take root, but our brotherhood stands firm."

Moving forward to place his elbows on his knees, he said, "Our blood talks to us down the ages. When I was a child, I would go with the Gypsies. They taught me, shared their wisdom and trained me in the arts. It was prohibited to spend time with them, had I been discovered, I would have been killed. So I would secretly slip away," the golden flecks in his green eyes sparkled as his pupils' dilated.

"Did your parents know?" I asked, moving towards him.

"They knew, but pretended not to know; there was no other way."

"The world is falling victim to mongrel criminals, whose far memories are steeped in blood."

Just then, a young Afghani woman pushed open the door carrying a tray. Her face was the color of a latte and her long hair as black as a raven's wing. She set down the tray of chi, cakes, cups and plates in front of us. As she began to serve, Aarif spoke in soft tones a few Afghani words; waving her away, he began to unload the tray himself.

"Can she speak English?"

"No," he said, handing me a china plate with blue violets hidden under a thick glaze.

These plates came long ago from England on a forgotten ship.

"We must free Afghanistan from the Russians by any means we can," he said, "That is my determination and my destiny, but to do so I am trading with devils."

"We both deal with demons, Aarif, for a greater cause, some inner instinct drives us."

"Help yourself to the cakes and chai," he said, waving his right hand over the laden table.

I picked up a tiny cup and poured in the sickly light brown chi from an old cracked teapot.

"We have this Saudi, Bin Laden; he has funneled money to us and helped build roads and tunnels. He's an agency man more interested in the powder trade than anything else. But with his help, we are awash with funds from the Americans and the British. Money, guns, everything just so long as we keep the poppy fields blooming and the powder flowing out through Pakistan."

"It's not much of an option," I said, "they want powder and to twist events and you want guns and training."

"Our fighters are being trained in Scotland, but the climate is poor."

"Yes, I heard. The Highlands are fabulous, but the weather is awful."

"I dream of returning to my horses."

He looked at the heavens and I know he saw the gray, black and bay Arab horses he loved racing in the skies. I could see them galloping in his eyes. Bringing his eyes back down, he looked straight into mine, "You alone can have one of my mares Tara. I promise you this; she waits for you."

"That is a fantastic gift Aarif."

"Now, in this sick world, someone also waits for you, he's from London,"

"I guessed as much when you asked me to bring my passport."

Aarif stood up and beckoned me.

"He's waiting in a room next to the kitchen, the women are

feeding him goat stew and rice and none of them speak English."

We chuckled together as we walked back into the courtyard, then passed through a small door.

Aarif withdrew, saying, "I will be in the courtyard."

The man from London sat on a wooden chair next to a table strewn with small bowls of food. As I entered, he rose to greet me.

"Good afternoon," he said, in an accent honed somewhere in the halls of Eton.

"Good Afternoon," I replied, motioning to the chair he had just risen from, "please."

He sat down again.

Placing the backpack on the floor, I took a seat at the opposite end of the table. In the background, I could hear the women chattering pleasantries.

His camel-colored suit hung from his frame a little too loose in places and a bit too tight in others. His freckled half-moon face had succumbed to the Indian sun and about it clung a bright red glow. He sat back down ramrod straight as if the chair was an unwanted guest.

"You have been enjoying some Afghani Cuisine," I said, to put him at ease.

"It has a little too much garlic for my taste."

"Does it really?"

"I've been sent out to see you."

"Indeed."

I had nothing in common with this young man, other than his birth had taken place in my country. My guess was he spent his time shuffling papers around, going to interminable meetings and delivering messages. That was what he was doing now.

"You are to catch the Aeroflot flight to London tomorrow morning," he said, handing me an envelope.

"It has all been arranged."

"Indeed," I replied, taking the proffered envelope, opening it, then rifling through the passport and plane tickets inside.

On opening the passport, my photograph jumped out with the name Anne Brown attached. The Birthdate made me ten years younger.

"You need to sign it," he said, taking out a silver pen from an inside jacket pocket.

Putting down the fresh dark blue passport on the table, I signed it. I knew the system and pulled out the passport I was using. These exchanges always made me feel somewhat vulnerable, but being caught with two different passports was worse.

"You will meet someone in Moscow, he will use the phrase Das Fingerspitzengefühl and you will respond verbluffend.

"Understood," I said, "but what does Das Fingerspitzengefühl mean."

"It means fingertip-feeling, an ability to empathize and interact with things and people."

"I will just be in transit through Moscow."

"Yes. The Afghanis will take you back to your hotel now."

Stuffing the Manilla envelope into the rucksack, I said a quick "goodbye," and returned to the courtyard where Aarif was waiting.

"You will need to pack," he said, as we walked to the entrance door.

Zaid was waiting on the Harley and ready to kick away the stand.

"Take great care of yourself Aarif."

He patted me on the back, "Go now, do not be a stranger."

Climbing behind Zaid I looked back at Aarif, framed by the giant door. Some foreboding told me we would not meet again. Then I was sailing away with the wind blowing through my hair.

4. HOSTAGE

"People can ignore reality but they cannot ignore the consequences of ignoring reality".

The screech over the Delhi Airport Tannoy shocked me out of my reverie, "Will Anne Brown, please come to gate nineteen immediately for boarding."

Damn, that's me. Had I been called before? The name Anne Brown was too new for me to answer to as a matter of course.

Springing out of the seat, I grabbed my baggage and rushed through the airport, avoiding the hundreds of men, women and children I passed.

Reaching the check-in desk for boarding, I proffered the smart girl with the pasted on smile the passport. She waved me through complaining, "The plane has been waiting for you on the runway for twenty minutes."

Quickening my pace, I was soon on the tarmac walking towards the jet, which stood white against the sun with a blue stripe down the side. As I mounted the movable steps propped against its fuselage, the peacock feathers I carried bend back under a flow of air. At the top of the steps, a Russian airhostess, her white-blond hair crammed under her small hat, greeted me. With a wave of her manicured hand, she indicated a window seat in the middle of the aircraft. If the passengers were annoyed at my late arrival, they did not show it. I settled down in my seat next to a black-suited Indian man in his forties, who stood up for me when I arrived.

"Sorry to keep you waiting."

"Not at all," he replied with a distinct Indian accent.

We were soon taxying down the runway and positioning for take-off. I enjoyed the rush through your stomach as the plane lifts off the runway to begin its ascent to the clouds. Fast cars with quick acceleration and aircraft, I loved it.

Once airborne, I took out a zipped plastic makeup bag and asked the Indian gentleman to excuse me. On my way to the bathroom at the rear of the plane, I noticed young Russians occupied the seats. As I passed by, their young fresh and serious faces turned towards me in an unnerving way.

Returning to my seat a hand reached out to rest on my arm. Looking down, I found myself locked into the diamond blue eyes of a young Russian girl.

"Hello, please sit," she said, motioning to a seat opposite which had just become empty. I settled into the grey and blue seat opposite her.

"Is this your first visit to Russia?"

"Oh, I'm just in transit."

Her features relaxed into inscrutability for a second, "We are the young communists. We are interested in your country, what do you do in your country?"

"Well, not much, I own some property."

"That is capitalist," she said.

"It is a capitalist country," I replied.

She and several of her colleagues stood up, "We are communists," they almost shouted.

"Oh yes, I understand," I said, placating them.

"What do you study in your country?"

Not briefed on what I was supposed to be studying, I leafed

through the pictures in my mind. One picture emerged of a book I had just read, 'The Secret Life of Plants' which is a fascinating study of the telepathic communication between plants and humans. *Well, they would not know anything about that.*

"I am studying the telepathic communication between plants and humans."

She fixed me with a disconcerting stare.

"I also study this," she exploded.

'Oops, not the best choice.'

"How interesting," I said, beaming at her with disarming friendliness, "we have so much in common."

My welcoming reaction put her off guard.

A boy behind us stood up, his shock of blond hair cut back off his face revealing startling ice blue eyes. Leaning over he handed me a gray plastic badge. I took it examining the raised symbol etched in yellow.

"It's St Petersburg," he said, retrieving the badge from my hand and pinning it to my jacket.

Some indefinable quality sealed our friendship as we chatted together. I fielded questions, feeding them insights into a world they could not conceive, music, nightclubs, champagne and films. They gathered around me and every so often would pin another badge on my jacket. Something told me that the gift of these simple plastic pins was a protection.

When I walked back to my seat the red jacket was encrusted with Russian badges and I had made some new friends. Settling back into the seat, lulled by the hum of the plane, I fell into a peaceful sleep.

Cutting brutally into my dreams the pilot's voice intruded, "We will be landing in Siberia."

Siberia; that was not a scheduled stop.

Pressing my nose against the glass porthole, I looked out; we were flying over a flat land of endless snow as far as the eye could see.

As the plane banked, a distant building came into view, its

enormous windows reflecting the sun's rays. The plane shuddered as we landed before the curious building, more an Arctic base than an airport. The sun shone in a cloudless sky, too cold for any moisture to raise up and float to become clouds. I imagined a Polar Bear or a winter coated Hare living here, but a human would not survive in the freezing, barren landscape.

The disembarking passengers started to file past me heading for the exit. All my new friends lined up along the gangway and exited in silence. Not one looked back at me or said goodbye. I did not have long to question why.

Russian soldiers stormed onto the gangway waving their rifles. The atmosphere charged with tension, jolting me into icy awareness. Two brown-clad soldiers stood guard one at either end of the aisle, with a soldier in the middle walking up and down. Their guns were turning this way and that as if threats were everywhere, although I felt the remaining passengers did not present a perceivable threat.

The Indian man next to me stiffened, staring ahead, struck dumb with fear. There was no point in trying to comfort him. The other passengers were terrified. A death like silence pervaded, no-one spoke and no one moved. *Something was wrong that was for sure and 'those bastards had bloody-well known it and said nothing.*

The prison camps in Siberia were legendary. I knew American prisoners of various wars struggled to survive the brutal cold. Sadness overshadowed me, thinking about these desperate men locked in Russia's prisons and mental hospitals. These brave Americans were collateral damage in a cold war that in actuality did not exist and neither side would help to free them.

The 'cold war' was an insider joke. Secret agreements meant both sides shared most things except Research and Development and political secrets. The elite cynically used the fear of nuclear annihilation as propaganda to control the populations of East and West. There were insiders and outsiders and the two sections lived in different worlds.

A man bristling with medals boarded the plane; he disappeared into the front of the aircraft, shadowed by the soldiers who handled his security. Within a few minutes, the plane taxied for take-off and the fear of incarceration in Siberia's prison camps receded.

As the plane made a bold rush for the sky, a small wave of relief passed through the passengers. The armed soldiers remained standing in the aisles, glancing around them with suspicion. These were not men trained to think for themselves. Tension in the cabin rose as people unused to this level of fear sweated trembled or froze. Animals can smell pheromones of fear; in this confined cabin, the fear was almost visible.

Looking out at the falling landscape below, I relaxed and closed my eyes. Awareness relies on calm, without awareness survival is more difficult. To keep the stench of fear from sparking a chemical reaction within me, I focused on my breathing. During the whole six hours, we had nothing to eat or drink provided and I was glad of the bottled water I always carried with me.

What seemed like an eternity, but was about six hours the captain announced, "We will be landing in Leningrad."

After touch down, the soldiers disembarked and tension in the cabin moved down a notch. However, we were all still hostages of the Russian Government. I picked up an odd whispered comment from passengers who felt they might hazard a few words to the person seated next to them.

"It will be Okay, "I said to the Indian man, whose name I will never know.

Remaining bolt upright in his seat, he glanced down and nodded. The fear he felt was simply too paralyzing for him to reply. *Was it a blessing or a curse that danger excited me.*

We did not wait long in Leningrad before the plane taxied for takeoff on another leg of the mystery tour.

One and a half hours later the pilot announced, "We will be landing in Moscow."

You could see the tanks as the plane landed. Gray-green monsters covering every spare inch of the airport. Anxiety mounted as passengers watched the circling tanks. The civilian airport I remembered was gone.

The plane came to a grinding halt. Armed soldiers boarded and began to unload the passengers. The nearest soldier motioned with his rifle for the Indian man and me to get up. We followed in single file down the gangway and on into the airport building.

Standing in line, with the other foreigners we moved inexorably towards two men in drab gray uniforms sat at a table. Soldiers stood watching over our line, adrenaline making them edgy and wary. Everyone kept their eyes fixed on the passenger in front of them.

When my turn came, I found myself looking at a seated Russian officer with blank eyes in an inscrutable face.

"Passport," he said.

I thrust the document into his large soft hands. Opening it, he glanced at the photo, raised his eyes to mine, stared for a moment and then snapped it shut.

"You will be staying in Russia," he said, slurring the English words.

"I have nothing pressing to do," I replied.

His eyes shot back to mine as the lightness of my tone swept over him. Then I moved on. There would be no connecting flight to London.

5 . NOT SO COLD WAR

"I worked for MI6 in the Sixties, during the great witch-hunts, when the shared paranoia of the Cold War gripped the services." John le Carre

Our overseer Olga, or so her name badge stated, was a young auburn haired woman. She herded us through the endless corridors of Moscow airport. Hanging in the rear of the group, I took the opportunity to count the number of tanks I saw through the airport windows.

To the side, a passage opened up leading directly to the runway. I left the group and turned down it straight into the barrel of a rifle. A soldier in his late teens with a soft down on his cheeks stared at me with pale, frightened eyes. Unable to speak Russian, I stood perfectly still so as not to scare him, time slowed down as I stared straight into his eyes.

"Nyet, Nyet." I heard, behind me in a sharp and worried tone. Olga appeared indicating to the soldier not to shoot. She rattled at him in Russian, his brow wrinkled, but he just kept the same startled position.

"Do not leave the group. You must not leave the group," she said, shepherding me back to the other hostages. Olga gathered us together and deposited us at the door of a restaurant.

Another girl arrived, handing Olga some cards. Beckoning to me, Olga pushed one into my hand and distributed the rest. There were forty people, but only fifteen cards.

Opening the restaurant door, she hustled us inside. Then

departed, closing the door behind her. We stood in a huddle momentarily lost without Olga's directions.

In charge of the Diner were two enormous Russian women who resembled female wrestlers. Their fat pink calves glistened beneath their white dinner-lady costumes ending in sensible black shoes. It was easy to imagine them in skimpy wrestler suits, with bulging thighs and breasts straining to escape

A long burnished steel counter ran down the right-hand side of the dining room. Yellow Formica tables with four plates per table littered the room, with uncomfortable looking metal chairs next to them.

Not bereft of all senses the hostages began sitting down at the tables. I sat next to a British couple. The man introduced himself as Ron. He presented his wife to me, but she had been shocked into silence.

The dinner ladies drove two trolleys with row after row of white eggs on the top and white bread underneath around the room. One arrived at our table; with a grimace, she snatched the paper from my hand and threw an egg and a piece of bread on my plate. We watched her leave in silent surprise. The card was a meal ticket. No card, no egg. Looking up from the white egg to the white faces of my companions, I said,

"That's just crazy, fifteen meal tickets for forty people."

"It is. What are we going to eat?"

"I just want to go home," his wife said.

"Do you know what's happening," Ron whispered, covering his mouth with his hand as if afraid the Russian women could lip-read.

"No, but I would not worry."

Having finished their rounds, the women retreated behind their counter, leaving their trolleys of eggs at the entrance to their steel domain. Fifty or so eggs sat on top of each cart cooling in the chill air.

Pushing my plate towards Ron's wife, I sprang up rushing towards the trollies. Grabbing four eggs, I shoved them into my jacket pockets and was back at the table passing them surreptitiously to Ron.

After the breakfast farce, we were herded onto a bus whose open door had long ago allowed any warm air to escape. The journey took us through an empty landscape with just a few snow-laden trees edging the road.

Drawing up at a hotel building we were shunted into a lobby. Armed guards watched over hostages from all over the world who sat silent, gazing in front of them.

Two soldiers ushered a German girl and me into a lift. No one spoke as the elevator ascended to the sixth floor. Escorting us to a door they steered us inside and closed the behind them.

The room was small, unadorned and functional with two single beds. To the right, a door led into a bathroom. Cold air blew in from a partially open window set high on the wall. The German girl sat down on the bed, putting her head in her hands.

"It's chilly," I said, striding over to the window, which hung open. Pulling the window too, it caught, and then just returned to its open position. The catch was faulty.

"Well, this is no good," I said to the silent girl who looked up at me with a blank stare.

She is not my contact.

"I'll go and get someone to fix the window."

If she understood me, she gave no sign.

Snatching up the soft leather handbag I carried inside the cabin baggage, I opened the door and stepped out.

Outside, the corridor was stark and empty, except for armed soldiers standing at either end. As I moved towards the lift, a soldier came to my side. I could hear the sound of the elevator moving up and down and the opening of doors on the floors below. The guard stayed with me until I reached the ground floor lobby.

Going to the reception desk, a grim Russian receptionist confronted me. The shoddy material of her black suit strained against rolls of fat.

"Hello," I said, "the window in the room will not shut."

She looked at me blankly.

I repeated, "The window in the room does not shut, it's faulty and needs to be repaired."

From under the counter, she drew out a sheaf of papers and began to write.

"Can you get someone to fix the window?"

"We must complete many forms for authorization," she continued to write. "What is your name and room number?"

I answered her questions while considering a list of hotel facilities on the wall. Midway down the list, a sauna jumped out.

"I want to take a Sauna."

"No, you cannot. At this time it is for men only."

"I'm shocked, I believed Russia was a country of sexual equality and I want to take a sauna."

She fixed me with a cold gaze tapping her fingers on the papers. Pushing them aside, she retreated into an adjacent room. I could hear unintelligible conversation coming from behind the closed door.

Returning to the desk, she continued to fill out the forms saying, "You can go to the Sauna when you want, it's on the second floor."

"Thank you so much," I said, leaving her to work.

Making my way to the second floor, I found the sauna. In the changing room, I undressed, clasped a short rough white towel around me and entered into the steam. Through the haze, the torso of a man came into view.

"Hello," he said, in English with a heavy German accent.

"Hello."

"You are very British, Das Fingerspitzengefühl."

"Do you think so, Verblufent," I replied, *what a strange place to meet a contact.*

"Welcome to Mother Russia."

"Thank you."

As the mist cleared a strong man in his fifties, with a craggy hard face and damp auburn hair, came into view. He would have been young during World War Two but I was certain his career began there.

"What is going on with the tanks and hostages?"

"Outsiders on both sides have upset the apples."

"You mean, upset the apple cart."

"Yes, right. The America movie star and Andropov are rattling sabers."

"But surely Andropov is an insider," I said, sitting down on a bench near to him, but at a respectable distance.

"He's a hardliner and intends to maintain his position. The Americans are pushing the agreements to their limits."

"As I understand it, we maintain Russia's nuclear facilities and share tech, but not R & D and Political espionage is forbidden."

"The agreements are in jeopardy," he said, wiping the sweat from his brow. "Right now we have a Perishing and SDI problem."[3]

"If Regan is the problem, then…"

"Reagan's useful; they may take action against Andropov."

"They're insane, but at least it keeps some balance."

"The few people who run the show follow set patterns, which are just as revealing as the patterns of life of a bear to a hunter," he said, staring hard at me through the steam.

"Indeed. Divide and conquer. Keep the population in fear, create an enemy, form a hierarchy, suppress uprisings, turn poor against poor, put your own people in place or blackmail leaders," I said as water vapor flattened damp hair to my scalp.

---

[3] On March 23, 1983, Reagan announced the Strategic Defense Initiative (labeled "Star Wars" by the media and critics). While Reagan portrayed the initiative as a safety net against nuclear war, leaders in the Soviet Union viewed it as a definitive departure from the relative weapons parity of détente and an escalation of the arms race into space. Yuri Andropov, who had become General Secretary following Brezhnev's death in November 1982, criticized Reagan for "inventing new plans on how to unleash a nuclear war in the best way, with the hope of winning it". https://en.wikipedia.org/wiki/Able_Archer_83

"It works perfectly by co-opting genuine feelings into a useful framework.

"We maintain the balance, for now," he said. "You will be sent home tomorrow."

"Not sure why they sent me here in the first place."

"Just remember what I said and don't throw anything away," he said, standing up and clamping the small towel around his waist.

"Okay."

"Enjoy your sauna and, safe journey."

He was tall enough to block out the light from the glassed door. Feeling a stark warmth emanate from this ruthless man, I knew I could sleep easy.

6. INTO THE FRYING PAN

"The Cold War was wildly expensive and consumed the entire globe."
David Remnick

A blast of cold air through the ill-fitting window woke me, turning over I glanced at the other bed. It was still empty. When I returned from the sauna last night, the German girl had gone.

Jumping up, I rushed to the bathroom and splashed cold water over my face. Today I was leaving for London and saying goodbye to this freezing hotel room. Shrugging on some clothes, I was out in the corridor, past the soldier at the door and heading for the hissing lift.

Down in the hotel lobby, I joined a group of hostages waiting to board the Airport shuttle parked outside the hotel entrance.

At the airport, they offloaded us like baggage into a terminal building. Two hundred or so abducted foreigners sat in rows of connected metal chairs. Like cinemagoers watching a horror movie, they were all silent. Fear hung in the air like fake snowflakes in a shaken glass globe. Taking a seat on a spare metal chair, I put my hand baggage on the floor. Next, to me, a man in a rumpled gray suit sat comforting a weeping young woman, who clutched a baby in a pink crochet shawl. Except for the slow course of tears rolling down her cheeks, all three looked as if they had petrified a thousand years ago.

From behind the drab gray wall at the front, a startling beauty emerged, neatly dressed in a blue and white airhostess uniform. Her long blond hair twisted behind her head, with the bulk of it struggling to remain clasped under a small-perched hat. In her white hands, she held a bunch of boarding passes. It was all too obvious to the abductees that twenty or so boarding passes would not be sufficient for two hundred people. Like the food tickets, this was a cruel form of psychological torture. Some of the hostages suffered daily transport from the hotel to view this pantomime.

A mature woman appeared, large breasts straining against her jacket buttons. With a flounce, she handed the beauty a piece of paper, which the girl scrutinized.

"Anne Brown," she called out.

Rising from the seat, I walked past the rows of shell-shocked hostages to arrive in front of her.

"Anne Brown?" she asked.

"Yes," I confirmed.

She handed me a boarding pass.

"Please return to your seat and wait."

Other names rang out breaking the silence; those named rose one by one to collect their boarding passes and return to their seats. It was a slow grueling process.

The gray man next to me stood up, shortly returning with his boarding pass. He reached out his hand to reassure the young mother. However, the next name was not hers, nor the next. Then, as the final name rang out her shoulders sunk, she stared ahead, glassy-eyed, clutching her rag-doll baby to her breast.

With a covert hunted look around the room, the grey man thrust his boarding pass into her hand. For a moment, her face lit up, then became impassive again.

At the front of the room, the mature woman returned.

"People with boarding passes come," she said beckoning.

"Follow me," I said, to the young mother.

She struggled to her feet, picked up her rather overlarge bag and dutifully followed.

"Stay a few steps behind me," I whispered.

Swinging my bag onto my shoulder and cradling the bunch of peacock feathers, I strode with a swagger to the front of the room. My flamboyant attitude had the power to divert their attention away from anyone else. Handing my boarding pass to the woman, she looked at me with undisguised distaste.

"Thank you for an exciting stay in Moscow," I said.

She was trying to work out what was so annoying about me long after I had walked down the long corridor towards the runway and several other less interesting passengers had filed past.

Strapping myself into the seat for takeoff, I pondered what would happen to the gray man and wished him well. As the plane glided through the skies with its cargo of hostages, I relaxed into meditation.

Eight hours later, we sunk beneath the ashen clouds to Heathrow Airport. The dazed hostages filed into an almost empty terminal.

No one approached us. Our return had been meticulously planned so that we would, "Ask no questions and tell no truths." The hostages passed through the terminal like sleepwalkers. There were no customs officers or checks.

When my luggage arrived in the recovery section. Placing it on a trolley, I made for the exit.

As the giant glass airport doors of swung shut, a rush of dank, damp air hurtled around me. Standing there shivering, I observed a black London taxi conveniently waiting. The driver got out of the pick-up car and without a word stowed the baggage in his trunk. Driving out of Heathrow, we passed rain splattered concrete and busy wet traffic. *I really miss the Indian sun*

Then the cab swung onto a smaller road, which ran past my old Approved School, Duncroft. The sight of the area where I had been drugged and tortured as a child stirred an avalanche of disturbing memories. These feelings killed awareness, made an agent vulnerable. However, right now I was not in immediate danger so could allow myself to experience emotions, which could spell death in the field. Closing my eyes, I let the soft hum of the engine and the gentle movement of the vehicle comfort and lull me to sleep.

Jolted into wakefulness I saw we had stopped before two large wrought Iron Gates. Entering through, we proceeded down a long drive shadowed by the branches of unkempt overhanging trees. The drive was broken in some places, beige, brown and green pebbles scattered the uneven surface like olives thrown over spaghetti. At the end, we turned right into a cleared gritted area. The car came to rest beside a set off stone steps leading up to a weathered wooden door. Stepping out of the cab into the cold, wet air, I cast my eyes over the rambling house. It was a tumbledown Manor in a state of disrepair. That this old house held secrets, I had no doubt. The great brown stained door swung open and an elderly lady stepped through. Her tweed jacket sported those indefatigable bobbles. Her blouse bulged at the waist leading down to a pleated tweed skirt and on to wool covered calves and flat brown shoes.

"Hello and welcome my dear, do come in it's so awfully nice to meet you," she said extending her hand.

Joining her on the steps, I felt her boney fingers grasp mine.

"Thank you. I have had a long journey."

She nodded to the driver to bring in the baggage.

"Indeed and you must tell me everything about it."

I followed her up old stone steps and into a bright room. Giant windows draped with red satin curtains, heavy with flowered motifs, hung down to kiss the ground. Each curtain was, caught up in a golden twisted band slung around a flowered catch. The carpet gave under my feet, red, yellow and green. I wanted to fling off my shoes and rub my feet into its rough-edged but soft depth. The focal point was a blazing fire of burning logs. Wooden sparks flew out highlighting the pinks and grays of the marble fireplace. Beside the fire was a side table laden with crumpets, sandwiches and a blue and cream tea set.

Old tapestry covered the armchair, into which I sank, its once vibrant colors faded by time to a mottled beige and dirty cream.

"I have had tea prepared, please help yourself," she said, handing me a blue and white plate with blue-veined flowers around the edge.

"Thank you."

With that, she sat down in the matching chair.

"What a lovely room."

"Yes, I spend a lot of time here."

Her eyes wandered to the antique bureau, the trestles and French polished tables.

"Now take a cup of tea and tell me all about it."

The debriefing had begun as she tweaked and twiddled out what I could recall. Time drifted into hours in the pleasant, cozy room.

The next day she told me, "We need you to go to sleep using your own identity, open a business or go on holiday."

"There are many things I have considered doing, but how safe am I."

"We will watch your back. When we need to reactivate you we will get in touch; there's a car in the garage, drive home and relax."

I felt myself weaving the strands of perception into images, sounds, feelings, smells as I climbed into the driver's seat of the blue Rover and turned the ignition key.

Leaning out of the window to wish her "goodbye," I realized a period of rest and relaxation lay ahead. I was at peace with that.

7. HIGH FIVE

Returning home from Sierra Leone late 1984, with cerebral malaria, I was under instructions to relax and recuperate. There followed five years of long days and nights of ordinary life, the soft fragrance of roses and strawberry's from my garden filled my heart with peace. The gentle summers and the wild winters were equally beautiful. Giant electric blue butterflies, quiet walks by the river, lying down at night on the damp grass to watch the stars, these pleasures feed the soul. My five hundred year old home and three-quarters of an acre garden was an oasis of calm, which enveloped me every time I stepped through the old red painted iron gates.

My working hours running a car lot with my friend Jules Ley had all the elements of a music hall farce. The car lot was part of a failed drive-in Burger bar, in Bangor North Wales. Having purchased the lease, Jules was trying to resurrect the business without spending a penny. Customers would drive up to the ordering intercom, which displayed a sign saying; press the button to place an order. When pressed they were instructed via a loudspeaker, to shout their order because the intercom did not work.

Today, the car lot and the Burger Bar were quiet. From the kitchen, mixed with the coffee smell, I heard Jules directing operations. Sauntering in through the open kitchen door, I saw Jules surrounded by a shambles of open freezers and hotplates. His girlfriend Kylie fussed around a mountain of buns, while a boy of uncertain age cleaned the counters with a dirty cloth. Meanwhile, Jules Old English

Sheepdog, Ben, inspected the burgers.

"Morning," I said.

Kylie looked up from the buns, "Hi Tara."

At eighteen Kylie was a beauty, her long blond hair fell in abundance over her toned body. She worried her bottom was too big, but its firm protruding roundness only added to her attractiveness.

"Hi, Kaz."

Kylie's great gift was her loving nature, abused as a child she once told me, "No matter what happened I always knew that God loved me."

"Tara," Jules said, turning around "do you want to buy the Honda?"

"Another cash flow problem Jules."

Pushing back his long brown streaked gray hair as it flopped into his eyes.

"Just a temporary glitch."

His colorful history of failed businesses had not daunted his entrepreneurial spirit.

"Ok, I'll take the Honda."

Ben, ambled over from his burger inspection to push against my legs, casually I stroked his matted fur.

"Ben needs a wash and Brush up Jules."

"You can do it if you want."

"If nothing is happening here I am going over to see Ivor."

"No reason to stay," Jules said.

"Okay, see you later," I said, exiting the kitchen.

I had recently acquired a Daimler which arrived with a fully paid up car phone via Danny, the scrap man. Its previous owner had fled to Spain for some misdeed. Sliding onto the Daimlers biscuit-colored leather seats, I sat for a moment casually watching the traffic. Life was simple, amusing and somehow complete.

The car phone rang, without thinking I picked up the cold black plastic receiver.

"Hello."

"Tara, it's time," Robert's voice cut through my pleasant day like cheese-wire through Cheddar.

The last time I had seen him was on a beach in Sierra Leone.

"Robert, it's you."

"We should meet near hallowed ground."

I knew he meant Bardsey Island. We had met there before.

"By the sea?" I checked.

"Yes, tomorrow at noon."

"Yes, OK."

The line went dead.

I had received the call. Memories flooded back dissolving away the peaceful years as if they had never been.

The next day I drove through the neat, welsh countryside down to the end of the Lyn peninsular. I parked overlooking Bardsey Island, green and blue glinting mysteriously under the sun's golden orb. This sacred jewel hung off the Welsh peninsula, as a pendant hangs off the neck of a beautiful woman.

Sacred to the old religion and the Christians, pilgrims from across the Kingdom traveled to Bardsey. A Monastery was built in 516 but had been destroyed by King Henry the Eighth. In legend, Bardsey was the final resting place of King Arthur, from which he would rise again. The waters around Bardsey are treacherous and deep, passable only at certain times. Rocks and crevices fought back the Irish Sea crashing waves turning them into cathedral spires and tunneled halls.

Stepping out of the Daimler the cool wind buffeted me, flattening the clothes against my body. I made my way to the steep steps leading to the water's edge, far below. A stillness inside me calmed the wind and my consciousness expanded, absorbing the power of the sacred island. Robert came into view, striding up the steps, smiling. Reaching the final step, he stood towering over me. A mountain of a man, his hair glinting red under the sun.

"Hi, Tara long time," his soft American tones drifted up to me.

"Hi, Robert."

In the way of warriors, we absorbed each other's essence, clasping hands in brotherhood.

"Do you remember the last time we met?" he asked, shielding his eyes from the sun.

"That unforgettable storm in Sierra Leone."

"And the ball of lightning."

The American embassy had the beach house right next to mine, on a private beach in Sierra Leone. Robert and I had watched a ball of lightning travel past us and go into the beach house.

"And the white-crested waves, appearing as the lightning cracked, then disappearing again into the moonless night."

"Magical Moments," he said. "Other than that it was a real backwater."

At that time, Siaka Stevens was President, but due to retire that year. Sierra Leone and neighboring Guinee were an intelligence hotbed. Coups were being planned so we monitored the worst of the soldiers of fortune and their co-conspirators.

"They stole all the aid. Remember the trawler donated by Japan, sold it to the highest bidder. Sacks of food to feed the hungry, auctioned off to the rich," I said.

"And the aircraft landing system, ruined when a Government Minister took the air conditioning units home."

"Yes and Mitterrand helicoptering in to tell Yves, it was all just a game and he should just spend the aid money on anything he liked," I said.

"So you all built the African Queen for jaunts up and down the coast," we laughed together as the breeze took our laughter out across the sea to Bardsey.

Robert sat down with a thud on the top step. I joined him fanning out my red and white polka dot skirts.

Turning to catch my eye, he said, "We need you to be recruited by MI5."

"MI5?" I gasped. "They are little more than police in drag."

"It will be easy for you."

"What do you want me to do?"

"Just watch and listen, do not make contact, we will contact you and of course watch your back."

"Okay."

"You will be approached by a man called Gareth Thomas."

"Okay."

"They will ask to borrow some of the cars off the lot. Say yes."

As I drove back to the car lot along the same twisty lanes, everything had changed. It was as if a door had opened to an alternate reality. I had entered into the world full of shadows and dark secrets, which lurked with menace in the corners of my mind.

Two days later I received a business call from Gareth Thomas. He wanted to hire some of the cars so could we meet. I agreed, suggesting the Yacht club in Port Dinorwic in two hours.

The Yacht club sat at the emotional heart of Ivor Jones's empire. Surrounding the club was a private housing estate, with a Hotel called the Pink Palace in the center. A river ran to one side deepening for harbored yachts, then on to a weir, a swing bridge and out into the Menai Straights. From almost every angle, the views were fantastic, as the eye caught the banks and waters of the Straights and distant mountains.

Driving down the steep, twisty, road to the yacht club, I contemplated this new turn of events in my life. Parking, I strolled by the harbored yachts with their main sails tossing in a summer wind. Even when wild winds set the yacht masts screeching out like banshees the place have a holiday feel.

The club entrance was a welcoming complex pattern of sparkling glass. Flinging open the door to the main bar,

"Where's Ivor," I said to the startled Barman.

"He's in the club," he told me continuing to buff a glass with a soft cloth.

Letting the bar door close on its own, I made my way through the foyer to the clubroom. In the darkened room, I spotted Ivor sitting at a table with July, his girlfriend of the moment. Ivor was in his sixties at the time and so was his wife Debby, but he had a stream of young girls interested in his money.

"Hi," I blurted moving towards their table.

A lock of Ivor's snow-white hair fell backward as he looked up at me. July's young face glistening with health remained immobile.

"I'm meeting someone in a few minutes and need some space to talk."

Ivor's long experience told him it was important but more than that, it might be interesting. As a Gemini, a lothario and a man of the world he always rose to the occasion.

"OK," Ivor said, "we'll put on the lights here and July can serve you coffee."

"Great," I said, "back in about two minutes."

When I returned, the lights were on and though empty the club looked open. I took up a position facing the door, at a small table near the honey-colored wooden dance floor. In a moment, July entered followed by a tallish, thin man with a languid athletic step, dressed in a dark grey suit. We locked eyes across the floor, as July ushered him to the table then withdrew.

I stood up and we shook hands.

"Gareth Thomas," he said.

"Pleased to meet you, please take a seat."

He drew out the chair opposite me and sat down, his long legs pushed out in front of him. His sleek black leather shoes with the leather cutout overlays slid under the table.

"I was given your name," he said. "We need the use of different cars every so often, maybe only for the day, Is that something you can do?"

"Yes, we can do that, cars come and go all the time and our insurance covers all drivers."

"That is useful. Would you be interested in working for our company?"

"What company is that?"

"Eagle eye, we do investigations."

Despite the cold, efficient front, there was something warm about him. Having psychic abilities always gives you an advantage in meetings, so I was aware of his feelings as well as listening to his words.

"Depending on the package I'm interested as long as it doesn't interfere with my work."

"No, it's part-time. We will only call on you when necessary."

"Okay, I am interested."

We were talking on two levels.

"What loyalty can the company expect?"

Sounds more like the Agency than 'five', and with a fictitious front company.

"That's a strange question."

"We need discretion."

"Oh, I have been trained in confidentiality."

"We may need you to discredit someone."

"Discredit."

"Yes, call their work and give them information that sort of thing," I raised inquiring eyes to him.

"We would never ask you to do something you were uncomfortable with," he assured me.

We agreed to meet the next evening in a pub in LLanfairfechan, when he would fill me in on the details. As Gareth walked out of the club and the door swung shut behind him, Ivor appeared from behind the connecting bar door. Leaning over the bar, he said,

"Well! Have you been recruited by MI5?"

"I think I have Ivor," I laughed up at him, "I think I have."

8. AFTER EIGHT

"The greater the power, the more dangerous the abuse." Edmund Burke

The smell of stale tobacco, beer and french-fries hit me as I entered the bar. Despite the early hour, the lounge was buzzing with people. I had been to this insignificant bar in Llanfairfechan once or twice and could think of no reason why Gareth Thomas had chosen it for our meeting. The entrance door, placed in the center of an elongated lounge, gave a full view of the room as you walked in. A high oak colored bar-counter spread the length of the lounge, with dark polished wooden tables and chairs dotted around in front of it. Light streamed in from the Georgian type white windows and a pleasant warmth covered me as I stepped inside.

Looking around, I spotted Gareth slumped in a dark corner behind a four-person table. His dress was casual, dark slacks with a black V-neck jumper, thrust over a blue shirt topped by his short coiffured mousy hair.

"Hello," I said, approaching the table.

Gareth rose to meet me demonstrating his good manners.

"Hello," he said, as we both sat down and looked at each other across the table.

His brow wrinkled.

"What would you like to drink?"

"White wine and soda thanks."

Sauntering over to the bar, he exuded an air of quiet confidence. You could tell his toned body from the way his slacks shaped over his high bottom. He brought back a full wine glass, transparent with a few bubbles clinging to the sides.

"Thank you." I said.

He began what seemed like small talk but was digging. The bar began to fill up as darkness fell outside. Street lamps began twinkling through the pub's little windows as we chattered. Then it hit, a light-headedness was washing over me, not one caused by alcohol. *Shit, it is a truth drug.*

Without a quiver on the outside, internally I rallied my forces. Gareth noticed nothing. From some dark recesses, I grasped at guidance from an unknown past and blithely continued unaffected by the drug, while giving the appearance of being under its influence.

He was firing questions, believing the drug had taken hold.

"Have you ever worked for the press or an intelligence agency?"

"No," I said, chattering away.

"We cannot have anyone with a criminal record or a member of the family," he said.

"I understand."

"What about your brother?"

"My Brother?"

Bruce was a Mason, but so were many police and security personnel, as far as I knew he did not have a record, but we were not close.

Ferrying his questions the night drifted past pleasantly as I began to enjoy the challenge.

Then I found myself alone standing outside in the cold night air, shaking my head to dismiss the drug from it. Laughing I walked over to the car, passing a middle-aged man in a green car reading a newspaper under the streetlight. Truth drugs and surveillance all so obvious with a distinct lack of professionalism

Over the next few weeks, the training began, surveillance, how to enter locked doors, investigation, and intelligence gathering along with instructions like…

"Never tell the Police anything, they can't be trusted," Gareth said, looking up and down the road.

"What if I get arrested?"

"If that happens, we'll sort it, don't worry about it," he said, with a dismissive wave of his hand.

As the months passed the fantasy that Eagle Eye was not part of the security services fragmented and disappeared. Then one bleak rain-splattered day Gareth called asking to meet in the car park behind the shops on Bangor High Street. The previous day he had handed me a photograph of the wife of a target, Terry Williams and asked me to get in touch with her. She had a young daughter but spent time in the Liverpool Arms Pub in Menai Bridge. Williams, who was involved with Bangor University and suspected of transferring biotech information to Iraq.[4]

The car park ran behind the shops in the upper part of the High Street. We always met at or around the back of Smiths Newsagents. Driving into the car park I spotted Gareth's Rover and parked in the next available bay. Getting out of the car, I walked over to his passenger door, sliding in beside him.

---

[4] In August 1989, the FBI raided the BNL office in Atlanta of the Italian Government-owned bank agency in Atlanta. Transactions relating to Matrix Churchill and its takeover by Iraq, as well as several other firms, including TDG, TEG, and Euromac, that the CIA linked to Iraq's clandestine military procurement network. The branch manager, Christopher Drogoul, was charged with making unauthorized, clandestine, and illegal loans to Iraq—some of which, according to his indictment, were used to purchase arms and weapons technology. He was subsequently sentenced to 37 months in prison.

Iraq, operating with an Italian-owned bank in the United States, obtained billions in credit from the state-owned, Banca Nazionale del Lavoro (BNL), the largest in Italy, funnelled US$ 5 billion to Iraq from 1985 to 1989. The U.S. branch of BNL made considerable use of U.S. loan guarantees.

Turning his clean-shaven face, smelling of a soapy aftershave, he said, "We're authorized to plant a listening device and search the target's place in Bangor. It's just over there."

He pointed to the rear of a building about twelve buildings to the right.

The target had been under surveillance for a few weeks, his habits tracked and a picture of his movements charted. We knew when he would be away from home. After eight, tonight it was safe to go in.

"We have the front under surveillance. The team will be here in ten minutes. The rear door is bolted, so no one can enter that way. But Dewi will let you in."

"You got authorization for the bug? That's an achievement."

Listening devices often disappeared, so a convincing retrieval plan was always necessary before authorization was obtained.

"Yes, finally," he passed me a buzzer.

"If there is a problem..."

Pocketing the small black shiny device it now lay next to a handkerchief and a tube of, red, orange, green, brown and yellow Smarties.

"Okay," I said, getting out of his car and returning to my own without a second glance.

After positioning, the car to view the rear exit of the building I took out the Smarties sorted out a red one and popped it into my mouth to suck slowly. Remembering how as a child, the red ones were used as lipstick making a big grotesque red orb over baby lips and around the mouth.

Dusk was settling over the car park as I strolled up to the targets rear door, waiting to hear the bolt slide open.

During the search, the team discovered hard drugs and a collection of child abuse images and videos. Whatever we moved or copied was put back in the same place, so the target would be unaware of the search.

The next day the videos described to me were child rape, including snuff videos, where a child would be raped, tortured and murdered on film. It was believed some of the child abuse images were of local children. Williams Company may or may not have been selling restricted technology to Iraq, but his involvement in the distribution of drugs and child abuse images was certain. It also became clear police officers were involved in protecting the child abuse image, distribution network.

Sitting holding some of these pictures, a pang of grief hit me. The frowns on my colleague's faces and the dark tension in the room wrote a dirge in my heart. We knew we would not be able to keep the evidence long. Letting the images drop back onto the table I stood up and walked out of the room.

Gareth was not far away, so I contacted him to arrange a meet in the park fronting Bangor Cathedral. Striding through the park the traffic outside made a low hum. Gareth sat waiting on a green painted metal bench so I slumped down next to him.

"You know what we found, the kids?"

He turned to look me in the eye,

"Yes."

"What are you going to do about it?"

"Nothing, it's not what we are after," he said, staring ahead.

The park now seemed dull, despite the profusion of flowers.

"Some of these children are from local children's homes, they say."

"That may be so, but what can we do?" he said, stretching out his legs and leaning back on the bench.

"So, basically you are going to do nothing to save these kids?" I said, feeling a tension begin to creep into my shoulders.

For years, I had known that the British security and intelligence services used children as blackmail tools. During the 80's and 90's, everyone was aware of child abuse by influential politicians. It was an open secret and openly joked about.

"Nothing can save them; they are an expendable commodity, sad as it is, it's not part of our job."

The Police, Special Branch, MI5 and MI6 and the Judges were determined to keep the awful system of systematic child abuse going.[5] With a sinking heart images of my childhood, over 25 years ago, tumbled into my consciousness, the abuse, the torture, the Police collusion. Yes, the Police always featured in it. Memories surfaced at first with unrecognizable feelings and then with an avalanche of emotions and clashing thoughts.

"Have to go," he said standing up.

I nodded, hiding the torment.

The cold metal of the bench caught my silent teardrops as I stood. Stumbling on through the park, into the street and back to the car. Nothing made sense anymore.

Driving over the white and green Menai suspension bridge, I made for Dwyran and a favorite parking spot overlooking the Straights. The beach was a city of rocks inhabited by a million barnacles clinging to life with crabs sheltering under stones and the sound of seagulls swooping as they twirled, buffeted by the winds.

Opening the window a sharp cold breeze sunk its teeth into warm cheeks, damp with tears. A dam had broken and emotions not felt since a child, welled over. Blinking back the tears, the sharp memory of that night in a Leeds Police cell twenty-six years ago stole my

---

[5] . Labour MP and Lord Mayor of London, Ken Livingstone in 1987 said that Captain Robert Nairac ran vice ring in Northern Ireland in the 1970s. This included children from Kincora Children's home.
http://hansard.millbanksystems.com/commons/1987/jul/07/northern-ireland-act-1974#S6CV0119P0_19870707_HOC_266 "We have to examine other allegations made on RTE that MI5 officers were engaged in undermining the power sharing Executive set up by the Government of the right hon. Member for Old Bexley and Sidcup (Mr. Heath). We have to look again at the allegations by Colin Wallace about the Kincora boys' home scandal. It has been suggested that young boys in a home effectively controlled by MI5 were buggered so that Protestant politicians could be blackmailed and silenced by MI5. That allegation cannot continue to drift around. It must be investigated and the truth exposed. The longer the British Government cover up and deny all this and refuse to investigate, the more the impression will be created that they know full well what has been going on and that far too many members of the Government are the beneficiaries of these acts of treason by MI5 officers in Britain and abroad."

thoughts.

Then the rocks, sand and waters returned to my screen of consciousness, black, yellow and blue, a tapestry of washed out colors. Life ebbed through my veins. Drying the tears I decided, if they would do nothing to help the children, then I would, authorized or not.

Leaving the Menai Straights I decided to call on Leya. She was a first-year student at the local University. Leya always cheered me up; her life was such happy chaos. Her Grandfather had bought her an apartment on Ivor Jones estate and a new Volvo. She lacked for nothing but wanted everything, which is how a young girl should be.

Past the Yacht club, over the swing bridge, I drove. Then onto Ivor's estate, green grassed areas, giving way to a profusion of flowering bushes in reds, golds and pinks. The rain had christened each leaf with a sparkle, as the sun, peeking through the rain-laden clouds caught the raindrops on their surface.

Leya opened her door, her shoulder length dark carroty red hair glowed under the hall light flaming her soft freckled cheeks and warm smile.

"Hi, Leya."

"Hi, Tara, what's happening?" some instinct telling her something was wrong.

"Give me a cup of tea and an after eight mint and I will tell you."

Following her into her lounge, we sat down on the sofa. Not able to tell her everything, I could still ask for her help. Her gregarious personality helped her make friends with all and sundry and despite her youth, she had a way of interacting with older people on an equal basis. In the past, Leya had confided that a family member was a pedophile, so I knew she would want to help.

One family group Leya knew, man, wife and two listless, unhappy looking kids, also owned an apartment on Ivor's estate. The wife was a mousy woman with an unpleasant habit of scowling. She confided in Leya, her worries about the illegal bodybuilding drugs her husband took and told her they hired porn videos from Darren Granger. It was an excellent place to start. Leya could show interest in the porn and find out if child abuse videos were available.

We decided to call Kylie as a third member of the team. Kylie had been an abused child and would want to help the kids. Combined with her beauty Kylie was brave, kind, outgoing and had a way of enchanting people. She arrived in a flurry of long golden curls.

We all three sat planning around a glass-topped coffee table.

"Together we'll make 'Charlies Angels' look trite and second rate," I said, looking at their sweet, eager faces.

9. UNSANCTIONED

Surrounded by tended gardens and tall deciduous trees, the car park of Seiont Manor Hotel stretched out to the front of the new building. Pippa and John Evans built the Hotel around the remains of an ancient manor house. The remaining three dark wooded rooms now formed the kernel of the modern Hotel.

Sparkling fountains, extensive gardens plus an artificial lake set the scene. The problem was it had been built in the wrong place so was without guests. Empty hallways, restaurants and bars. Empty sauna, steam room and gym leading to an exquisite indoor pool, lined with arched windows, which began at floor level and towered two stories high.

With their wealth dripping away there was nothing left to do but drink the champagne from the extensive cellars, use the facilities and enjoy the setting. Pippa and I spent hours talking in the old library, served with smoked salmon sandwiches, exquisite cakes and vintage champagne.

Today Pippa and I sat as usual in the library examining her and John's natal and progressed astrological charts. Her long blond hair fell forward, obscuring her patrician face as she pointed one elegant manicured hand at the symbol for Pluto.

"Pluto is placed to strip away the illusions in your life giving you an opportunity to divest yourself of material things and find the alchemical gold within."

Her hazel eyes looked into mine with a knowledge of a thousand worlds and eons of time. We had paused in the now.

"Madam," a voice from a different world intruded.

Turning, I saw the receptionist in her black skirt and crisp white blouse with brown hair held back in a bun.

"Yes?" Pippa said.

"Tara has a telephone call at the desk."

"Oh, thank you," I said, "I'll be there in a moment."

Pippa let her gaze fall back to the charts.

"Doesn't it always happen just when you step into the other world?" I said, rising, letting a few stray crumbs fall onto the floor.

The smaller reception desk stood to the left of the Hotel lobby. The girl in a black skirt and white blouse handed me the receiver.

"Hello?" I said.

"Tara?"

"Yes."

"It's Nick Lewis," the voice said, as I placed the crème receiver to my right ear.

Nick Lewis was a police officer in his late thirties. Tall and brash with the arrogant forcefulness of those who know the Public front of the Police is a complete fraud. I had not found him likable.

"Hello Nick, what can I do for you?"

"Someone would like to meet you," he said.

"Okay."

"Can we meet tomorrow at the Bridge in Caernarvon?"

"Yes, I can do that at about noon. Would that suit?"

"Fine, see you tomorrow."

"See you," I said, replacing the receiver.

I had first met Detective Constable Nick Lewis at Seiont Manor. He was a drug squad officer, which is a euphemism for the team who control the supply of drugs. Just as the anti-terrorist squad is a euphemism for directing terrorists. *To what strange twist of fate did I owe this call to meet today?*

The next morning I drove past Caernarvon Castle. Apart from the towers, the castle was in ruins. It was the place chosen for the Investiture of the royal supplanter named as Prince of Wales. Built in the 13th century by the English king Edward the First who invaded North Wales in 1283. The Castle remains a symbol of English oppression.

A floating, pontoon boat restaurant, with porthole windows, snuggled close to the dock. Waiting, rocking gently, for tourists to board it. Long ago, I had taken dinner, sitting next to a porthole window, but now the memory was so vague I had forgotten with whom I had dined

The swinging footbridge spanned the few yards from the dock outside the castle walls, over to a promontory on the far side. Between these two points, the waters of the River Seiont flowed towards the coastline of Anglesey. The bridge glowed white and green in the sunlight, its humble span with the castle backdrop giving it a fairytale quality. Stepping onto its light brown floor, the expanse ran out in front of me, white edged with green metal railings, empty and clean. Reaching the middle, I leaned nonchalantly over the railings, as if my objective was to view the waters below.

From my peripheral vision, I saw DC Nick Lewis and a smaller, fatter, older man with him approach the bridge. Caernarvon Police Station is a dark building of dour dressed stone huddled beneath the Castle escarpments. It was a short walk for Nick and his friend to the bridge I waited on.

As they approached, I maintained the dramatized gaze over the bridge parapet. They shuttled towards me like billiard balls coming to rest one on either side of me. I did not look up.

"You wanted to meet."

"This is DI Maldwyn Roberts," Nick nodded at the smaller fatter man.

I inclined my head towards the portly figure on my left with the pepper and salt hair and the round face.

"Hello, Maldwyn, What can I do for you both?"

Nick, letting his senior officer take the lead, positioned his elbows on the railings giving the pretense of casual water gazing.

"We want you to infiltrate the satanic abuse rings," Maldwyn said.

"What?" I exclaimed in surprise.

"We can't pretend to be a fifteen-year-old girl."

"Well, neither can I."

"It's a Home Office Directive."

"Is it?" I said, flashing him a sideways glance.

"The Home Office wants something done about satanic abuse and we need you to organize it covertly."

"It's unusual for the Home Office to take this sort of action."

"It's become an issue and something needs to be done."

"Look, I am interested in this so I will do what I can. What about child abuse and the videos?"

"The directive is restricted to ritualized abuse, we are not able to move on the videos right now," he said, running his hand over the railing where it had come to rest.

"Okay, but it needs to be taken as a whole."

"You know how to investigate this; it needs someone with your background, so we are authorized to ask you."

"What about confirmation?"

"I will confirm the Home Office directive," Maldwyn said, "You can have my number; they can phone me at Caernarvon Police station."

"And you are the divisional inspector?"

"Yes."

"I've been told not to work with the Police, but if this is a directive..." I let the sentence trail off.

"We will be grateful."

"Why are we meeting in secret if you are authorized?"

"We do not know 'who' is involved, so can we keep this between us?" he asked, reaching into his pocket.

"Okay. That I can understand."

"You can call me anytime at this number, or use it for confirmation," he passed me a handwritten number on a piece of paper; "it's my direct line."

Taking the number, I slipped it into my pocket.

Maldwyn and Nick moved off without a second glance passing over to the far side of the bridge. Anyone watching would have seen two men have a casual conversation with a stranger on a bridge before walking on.

Walking back to the car my head was full of questions. Satanic abuse was a hot potato. Just two years before the Cleveland Inquiry, headed by Judge Lady Butler-Sloss who's pedophile protecting, brother Sir Michael Havers was Attorney General at the time, [6] had put the lid on any question of satanic abuse. The report she produced at great expense to the taxpayer and considerable personal profit presented the fiction that the Cleveland Inquiry had looked at the allegations of satanic abuse and found none. In truth, pliant legal professionals had predetermined the answer that it did not exist.

Considering this recent background, I was surprised the Home Office wanted an investigation. As an organ of Government, it was notorious for facilitating child abuse, PIE (Pedophile Information Exchange) magazine MAGPIE had been published from its own offices.

I drove into the Burger Bar it was quiet, Kylie came out of the kitchen her golden hair catching a ray of sun as it bounced off a car wing mirror. She waved as I drove up and parked next to her.

---

[6] Butler-Sloss had to withdraw from the on-going Child Sexual Abuse Inquiry because her brother was criticised for covering-up child abuse as Attorney General. https://www.theguardian.com/society/2014/jul/14/lady-butler-sloss-stands-down-child-abuse-inquiry

"Hiya."

"Hiya Kaz."

"I have something to tell you, let's go and have a coffee somewhere."

"Okay, I'll get my bag it will be good to get out of here."

"Where's Jules?"

"He's looking at a car."

"Let's go to Carreg Bran."

"Okay, I will take my car," she said, rushing back into the kitchen to reappear a few seconds later with her brown leather bag slung over her shoulder and her car keys in her hand.

The Bran was a restaurant in a small hotel not far from the banks of the Menai Straights. I drove first into the car park and Kylie parked next to me. It was lunchtime and the car park was half-full with diner's cars. The food was not bad, but as a vegetarian, there was little for me on the lunchtime menu.

We ordered coffee and took it outside to the picnic type tables.

"Guess what?"

"What?"

"I had a secret meeting with the Police today they said the Home Office wanted an investigation into ritual abuse and asked me to help."

"That's great," she said. "What can I do?"

"Ask around; see if you can find out anything, but discreetly."

Kylie had grown up in the area and developed contacts everywhere, her beauty, vibrant personality and loving nature gave her inroads into many hearts.

"We'll tell Leya later, so we can all work together on it."

'Charlie's Angels,' Leya, Kylie and I began to gather evidence. North Wales, it seemed, was a haven for pedophiles, perverts and criminals of all persuasions. Investigating such darkness and depravity meant our shield of light had to be as bright as the sun. We soon found that if we dropped our shields, shadows in the corners would come alive with demonic force.

The girls discovered a Pastor in Holyhead, on the Isle of Anglesey, who was shielding victims of ritual abuse. I gave him a telephone call.

"Good morning, I understand you have a problem with child ritual abuse and are helping some victims."

"Who told you about that?" he said, a shake in his voice.

"I have been investigating child abuse for the Home Office."

"The Home Office?"

"Yes, a directive has been issued to gather evidence so that effective action can be taken."

"Before I say anymore or meet you I need to confirm this Directive Exists."

"I understand it is a wise precaution," I replied, "you can check with Divisional Inspector Maldwyn Roberts at Caernarvon Police Station."

I gave him Maldwyn's number and my own.

"I will phone DI Roberts and get back to you," he said, putting the phone down.

The moment the phone was down, I rang Maldwyn.

"Hello Maldwyn Its Tara, I've found a pastor in Holyhead with information he is going to telephone you."

"Right, I will confirm the directive for him."

Thirty minutes later the Pastor rang me back and we made an appointment for the next day in Holyhead.

The boy was about sixteen years old; hands trembled as he clenched and unclenched them on his lap. Looking at him, his fresh face and the slight body was that of an average youth, except for his tormented, haunted eyes.

"In your own time tell me what happened?" I asked.

"They would take us to the Church," lowering his eyes as If trying to avoid contact with unimaginable pain.

"A church?"

"It's in a lonely place, with no-one around."

An image rose up in my mind of a small, isolated church surrounded by old Yew trees bent and knurled with age.

He continued gripping the sides of the chair as children do at the dentists.

"A pentagram was drawn on the floor the adults dressed in black robes, that was where I was raped and tortured."

"When did it start?"

His face crumpled to resemble a discarded plastic supermarket bag.

"I was four," he said.

Like his face, my heart crumpled. I wanted to reach out to comfort him, but dare not. A physical touch of empathy and love may only remind him of the pain.

The pastor's charges lived in abject fear. Their lives haunted by their abusers, whom, they said, held senior positions within the Establishment. Even the Pastor was too wary to name the abusers to me.

Driving home, I contemplated breaking the satanic rings. Their rituals and festivals were a sick parody of ancient Celtic pagan celebrations. Satanists believe, the essential nature of the universe is based on energy and vibration, they would rape and murder on specific dates, in specific places of power. This dark practice began in ancient times. Child sacrifice was practiced in the Americas, the Middle East and Europe. Crawling down the centuries from a barbaric past, it is well documented to be a growing practice in South Africa and Uganda. How widespread these practices were in 20th century Europe I did not know.

That, enclaves of insane pedophiles and black magicians existed I had no doubt. Satanists believed their power was fortified by the death throws and terror of innocents. The very betrayal of all was good, pure, loving and caring marked their laws, rituals and debauched lives. My own experience had taught me that the occult element was embedded in the organs of government like the name Blackpool through a stick of candy rock.

Gareth was away but had given me a secure number, which I could call in an emergency. The next day I called to let him know what I was doing.

"Hello, Gareth."

"Hello."

"It's not strictly an emergency, but I want you to know what I'm doing."

"Yes?"

"The Police contacted me."

"The Police. Why?"

"They wanted my help to investigate Satanic Abuse they told me it was a Home Office Directive and I was well placed to do the investigation."

"You should not be communicating with the Police," he said a steel clip in his voice, "look; I will check this out and get back to you. In the meantime, do nothing more on this."

"Okay," I said, "I will wait until you get back to me."

Having placed the telephone receiver back into its rocker, I went to the laden bookshelves to see what I could find out about ritual sacrifice and the dark arts. Mother and I were avid collectors of volumes on the occult and the library was extensive. Many books were short runs or out of print.

Taking down one small paperback with an occult symbol on it of a ritual dagger, I cuddled up into a big leather chair with my feet dangling over the arms and began to read. The book exposed an Extreme right-wing Monday Club being involved in child abuse and ritual sacrifice. There were some graphic details and well-known names mentioned in the book. The research was moving towards a network of influential people involved in unspeakable acts.

The book hinted at a Masonic brotherhood of occultists who sat at the center of the British Empire web spinning a fabric of lies to manipulate the population and their belief systems. As for child abuse with a ritual element the brotherhood used mind manipulation to make people believe ritual abuse existed in the minds of the mad, the deluded and the divisive. A covert system, with its flawed law and order ethos, pliant judges and propaganda closed down all investigations from social workers and all complaints from abused children and their erstwhile protectors.

The pages also revealed details of Operation Paperclip, which brought Nazi Scientists into UK and USA to conduct secret mind control programs. It all reminded me of 'Gladio'. *Was there some agreement between the dark side where occultists, Nazi scientists, security services and Satanists gathered under one umbrella of shadows and terror with little children as prey.*

As I read, I became intrigued as to why the Home Office wanted this investigation into ritual abuse. The phone rang. I went into the hall and picked up the receiver.

"Hello?"

"Tara," Gareth said, "There is no Home Office Directive."

"None?"

"No. The Police lied."

"But why?"

"They are doing this on their own because they are involved," he said. "The Home Office knows nothing about it and you must 'not' work with the Police or pass them information."

"OK, but what about the investigation? I have found some interesting leads."

"You must close this down. Child abuse is not on our agenda."

"Ok, thanks for checking," I said, putting the receiver down.

With finality, it dawned on me, what I should have known, but somehow did not, that cover-up of child abuse of all kinds was more revealing, more complex, convoluted and insidious than the abuse. Without the systematic and organized cover-up of the abuse by the Police, the abuse and child abuse image trade could not have continued. Obviously, the abuse and cover-up were supported by a network of pedophiles and a wider criminal network involving elements within Police Forces, State Agencies and Government itself.

10. ALARMING NEWS

"Behind the ostensible government sits enthroned an invisible government owning no allegiance and acknowledging no responsibility to the people. To destroy this invisible government, to befoul the unholy alliance between corrupt business and corrupt politics is the first task of the statesman today." Theodore Roosevelt

Waiting for Colin to arrive in a deserted hotel lobby, I stood looking into a giant gold-framed mirror twice my size. The shimmering gold of my hair became lost, in the gold lacquered frame of flowers. My dress of blue velvet, sewn with lighter blue twirls of silk roses, dripped into the sunlight, splashing onto the mirror like a summer sky. Any moment I expected to step through the mirror and meet a white rabbit, but in my heart, I was not Alice. I was more the fantastical creatures Alice met than the girl who encountered them.

Behind me a dark-suited figure loomed, I was no longer alone. Colin was still young, but like most Special Forces, he felt that aged thirty-eight he was just too old. There is something feral about men, who can fight and win physically. Men who win with their minds seem depleted, their strength zapped by endless worries and pointless objectives.

He nodded into the mirror without speaking. Turning I inclined my head moving to his side. We began to walk in one seamless movement down the hotel corridor. Telepathy is a gift between loved ones and between those who, live in the world of shadows and mirrored halls. Glancing up at him, he gave the impression of a trained police dog pretending to be a pet. No amount of gray suit material could hide the toned hard muscular frame beneath.

"How are you, Tara?"

"Fine," I said as we continued along the corridor, passing portraits of long-dead people.

"Your child abuse investigation has exposed you, but that is an opportunity as well."

"Are you going to do something about the kids?"

"Not right now we cannot," he said, "what we want is for you to go and convince the Opposition that the Government is selling arms to Iraq."

"Is it something to do with PRB?" The factory was producing propellant for Gerald Bull's Project Babylon (Supergun) amongst other covert deals. PRB was part of EASSP a Belgium cartel funneling explosives to Iran and Iraq.

"Not specifically," he said, "but it's part of the exposure we are going to make."

Gerald Bull was a Canadian weapons scientist and owner of SRC a company linked to NATO's secret Intelligence service. He had wanted to Buy PRB, but the British Government intervened to stop him. Bull's offer of GBP £38 million for a 51% stake in PRB but was refused but Astra's offer of £20 million for 100% was taken instead.

"Gerald James arranged the purchase of PRB for Astra without knowing the end purpose," I said.

"Yes, we are aware; all the usual suspects were behind preventing Bull from getting PRB." [7]

"Let's face it Bull smelt a rat and those rats walk up and down the halls of parliament," I said, " PRB's parent company SGB had the same Whitehall address which 6 (MI6) use, the whole thing is a slap in the face."

---

[7] Lobster Journal of Parapolitics. Page 16 and 17
www.8bitmode.com/rogerdog/lobster/lobster31.pdf

"Yep and now all PRB's work has moved to the Belgrade Industrial Complex, it will fuel another conflict no doubt," he said.

"No doubt," I agreed, shaking my head.

"It's time to expose the covert routes and the Labour Opposition is best placed to do that," he said, "your job is to convince them that the Government is breaking the embargo, and then engage with the media. After that we want you to get in touch with Andre Cools and pass him information."

"Andre Cools?"

"He's the former Deputy Prime Minister of Belgium," he said, glancing down at me.

"Yes of Course I remember."

"Andre Cools will investigate PRB he wants to suss out why Belgium has become a portal for the global trade in illegal arms."

"Okay, what about the evidence."

He paused as we sank in silent unison onto two cane chairs upholstered with crème cushions, which stood in the hotel hallway.

From his inside coat pocket, he drew forth a small bundle of folded documents.

Taking and unfolding the crisp paper, photocopy sheets a diagram of a giant gun emerged. I had seen something similar in the Bagdad trade fair a few months ago. It was a smaller version of the 1000 mm Supergun.

"Project Babylon."

"Yes, it's the 600 mm," he said.

"Not the 350mm Baby Babylon, it reminds me of Alcester Crowley's whore of Babylon, I'm sure that's just what they intended. It's part of the Allivane network or as they call it, All in Vein."

Fanning out the other documents, I noted the name Carlos Cardoen, a Chilean arms dealer/manufacturer and South American warlord. My Brother-in-law, John Penny, worked for International Signals and Control (ISC); they supplied arms via Cardoen to Iraq. Other documents dealt with PRB, Astra and Allivane.

\

"Mark Thatcher is involved with Cardoen," I said, "and Cardoen is using fake end-user certificates in favor of Jorden and Saudi to deliver to Iraq with ISC supplying Rockeye and cluster bombs through him."

"Yes Cardoen is key to unraveling the covert game, just convince them Thatcher and the Government are selling arms to Iraq."

"These are just snippets," I said.

"It's all they need to see before we are sure they will take action," he said, "Politicians are always out to feather their nests, just convince them it's true, they can investigate themselves."

"Am I able to explain the process to them without issue?"

"You can sing like a bird," he laughed, "when the time is right, more of the documents will be made available, but do not part with any documents until they tell you what they are going to do."

"Okay, I will go and see Kinnock."

Neil Kinnock was the leader of the Labour Party.[8]

"Good, you should use your birth name."

He stood up, his shock of blue-black hair falling over his sky blue eyes, "we will be in touch," he said, leaving me fingering the photocopies.

The next morning the air was still cold as I dressed in a smart light blue mix cotton and wool suit, long gray leather boots and a black Cashmere coat with a neatly fitted waist and fluted skirt.

Neil Kinnock lived in a detached house next to a green Common in Ealing, a quiet residential leafy suburb of London. The common is a broad green swathe surrounded by houses with gardens. Around the edge of the grass, a concrete path circled, here residents walked their excited dogs as others jogged in sports gear and young mothers pushed Prams. It was an oasis of green and waving flowers in beds where local

---

[8] The Labour Party was the main opposition party in the UK Parliament then.

people could make contact with nature.

As I walked towards the common, the spring sun broke through the fluffy clouds chasing them away as it rose higher into the sky. Standing in front of Neil Kinnock's dwelling, I observed an ordinary detached red brick house. Flicking open the metal gate catch I walked the short distance to the green door and rang the bell.

Waiting for an answer, I was aware of the rivers of time rushing in upon me. Exposing my identity was a fatal step. In my handbag, twenty documents lay snuggling next to a gold-plated powder compact with the little catch that made it spring open to reveal inside the mirror a hidden camera.

Neil Kinnock opened the door, his ruddy face with a hint of freckles a little flushed.

"Good morning Mr. Kinnock."

"Yes," he said, avoiding direct eye contact.

"The government is illegally selling arms to Iraq. Will you expose it?"

He looked shifty, a moment ago; he was idly focusing on the cute woman at his door now his awareness heightened. Looking furtively up and down the path, he stared with suspicion at his tall green hedge as if paratroopers might be hiding there.

"Yes, if you have evidence." [9]

I tapped my handbag in answer. Kinnock looked into my eyes for the first time to catch the truth. He knew truth from falsehood and he had dealt with people from the intelligence world before.

"Leave me your phone number and I will get Allan Rogers to contact you."

Drawing out a card, I pressed it into his hand.

---

[9] Neil Kinnock MP, in August 1990 , after he knew the Conservative Government were illegally selling arms to Iraq deceitfully supported the UK and USA in a call for war with Iraq. Then in early 1992 Kinnock again had the opportunity to rock the Tory Government for breaking the arms embargo to Iraq and win the General Election, instead his silence handed the election win to the Tories.

"Allan Rogers will call you," he said and with a final furtive glance around his garden, he closed the green painted door.

It was a disappointing meeting if meeting it was. Neil Kinnock appeared more like a criminal talking with a drug dealer on his doorstep than a senior politician and leader of a party and possible Prime Minister. I did not trust him.

As promised Allan Rogers MP did make contact and we arranged to meet at Mornington Crescent, a little used London underground station.

The tube door opened onto an empty platform. Mornington Crescent is a lonely tunnel, deep under the streets of London, its emptiness creating a strange and stark atmosphere. Stepping out of the tube, I felt the swirl of heated air as the pneumatic doors closed behind me. In front, lay the deserted platform, a smell of fetid air wafting around as the tube disappeared. Leaving the swish and hiss of distant tubes rushing through another tunnel somewhere. I had stepped into the 'twilight zone'.

To the far left, a man of medium height, whom I recognized from press cuttings, stood dressed in a dark suit. Turning, I walked towards him. We could have been secret lovers or drugs dealers meeting in a lonely place, but he was a Labour MP and I was the agent of a service whose existence he may never know.

We came face to face on that empty platform under London.

"Tara Davison?" he said, extending his hand.

"Allan Rogers?"

We shook hands like explorers who had met for the first time on a lonely mountain but were unsure if they would be friends.

"Sorry about the venue," he said.

"It is entirely appropriate for what I have to say."

"I am all ears."

"Quite simply Alan; the Conservative Government is illegally selling arms to Iraq, in collusion with the Americans and vast personal profits are made via kickbacks."

He smiled wryly, "Interesting."

"Thatcher and her son are fully involved; it's a no holds barred weapons sales, Cluster bombs through Cardoen Industries in Chile as well as Rockeye, Biological and Chemical weapons tech transfer."

Watching him for hints of emotion or unease, there were none. *Did he already know much of what I disclosed?*

"They're building Iraq a military industrial base and a fuse line and have sold Iraq a huge gun, which has an orbiting nuclear capacity and has been banned by treaty."

"What evidence do you have?"

"Twelve thousand documents proving the illegal trade, false end-user certificates, letters, diagrams and transactions, unequivocal incriminating documents."

Reaching into my handbag, I drew out the now crumpled photocopies.

"I have with me sample documents."

Handing them to him to allow him to leaf through them.

"What's this?" He asked.

"That's the schematics of the 600mm Project Babylon a huge gun. Before I part with any documents or provide you with others, I need to know what you are going to do."

"That's not a decision I can make on my own Tara."

"I appreciate that, please discuss it and let me know as soon as you can."

"Why are you exposing this?"

His studied composure beginning to slip as perhaps the enormity of what he saw engulfed him.

"There are those who want it exposed."

"It's a dangerous business."

"I do not minimize the danger it places me in and now you. Arms sales make big, big money and the kickbacks are king's ransoms secreted away in offshore bank accounts."

He looked at me taking in what I was disclosing. *'Just how much did he already* know?'

"We need you, to bring this up in the House," I said.

An approaching tube set dancing a turbulence of warm putrid air. The green doors hissed open like an angry snake, entering I left Allan Rogers standing alone on the deserted platform.

I was staying with Pippa in Ealing Broadway. Her hotel project Seiont Manor had sunk. Pippa lost the hotel, and her marriage broke up. John ran off with another woman, bought a yacht and was living somewhere in Ireland. Pippa had a new love in her life, a psychologist called Yuric, who welcomed me into his home.

On my way to Pippa's, I was aware of the surveillance, a gray-suited man peeking at me from behind a newspaper, a casually dressed couple loitering near the tube exit to Ealing Broadway.

The apartment was empty when I arrived. Depositing the shopping on the floor, I sank into an armchair for fifteen minutes of meditation. Lifting my consciousness, the dark specters of arms sales, drugs, sex trafficking, terrorism and deception fell away. The insistent ring of the phone brought me back to the world of sight, sound and smell with a jolt. I picked up the receiver.

"Tara?"

"Yes?"

"Do not go out tonight. Bull has been taken out after a meeting with Gumbley the MD of Astra."[10]

"What has this to do with me?"

"The same time you were meeting Allan Rogers, Grumbly was in Belgium meeting Bull. They were developing a strategy to expose the trade and protect themselves from the British Government."

My head began to spin; thoughts and emotions tumbled over each other as I reeled under the contained shock. Bull and Gumbley were another leg of the exposure process of which I was involved and that

---

[10] Bull returned to his apartment when three shots were fired by a silenced 7.65 mm handgun into his back and two into his head

leg had been ruthlessly cut off at the hip.

"Understood," I said, replacing receiver. [11]

---

[11] Gerald Bull left his meeting with James Gumbley Astra's MD, they arranged to meet again with Gerald James Chairman of Astra to plan a joint strategy to expose the cross Atlantic illegal trade in arms. Bull was compiling a list of Politicians in Washington and London who took kickbacks. To disguise the source kickbacks were paid to family members. One listed name was Mark Thatcher, other prominent names on the list were Peter Levene, Jonathan Aitken, and George Younger.

11. LADY OF THE LAKE

"Death is not the greatest loss in life. The greatest loss is what dies inside us while we live." Norman Cousins

It was scarcely two weeks since I had left Allan Rogers MP on the lonely station platform when Superguns huge barrels were exhibited on BBC news. UK Customs had seized Lorries carrying parts of the giant 1000mm gun to Teesport Docks.[12] *Well, the plot thickens.*

When the broadcast concluded, I rushed into the office to get the copy of the 600mm supergun schematics. Opening the desk drawer, I ruffled through the papers. It was gone. Taking out all the documents, I spread them out on the desktop searching. White paper leaves tumbled to the floor. No, it was definitely gone. "Bastards," I mumbled under my breath. *"I would have to get another copy."*

Avidly, I watched the news as the seizure of parts of the biggest gun in the world hit the headlines. The Government, so deeply embroiled in the illegal arms trade with Iraq, feigned shock at the discovery.

Then, they did what the corrupt Western States usually do. They announced an inquiry. Whether its illegal arms sale, systematic rape of

---

[12] 21st April 1990 parts of a Supergun ddiscovered.
http://news.bbc.co.uk/onthisday/hi/dates/stories/april/11/newsid_2477000/24
77023.stm

children or corruption of any kind an Inquiry will stifle debate and allow the cover-up squads to move in. For Supergun, they convened a Parliamentary Select Committee to look into the affair. Select Committes crammed with fellow politicians can be even more useful for hiding the truth than pliant judges.

The Super Gun had made its debut in 1989 at the Bagdad Arms fair. Where military personal jostled with hard-faced men in expensive suits to listen to salesmen, talk about the deadly weapons they sold.

The UK Department of Trade and Industry headed by Trade Secretary Nicolas Ridley had sent seventeen British Companies to display their wares alongside Gerald Bulls Company SRC (Space Research Corp). By sending British Companies to display their military hardware in Iraq, they were cocking a hoop at their own official embargo.

Supergun stole the show when SRC unveiled a 1.5-meter scale model of supergun (project Babylon) complete with tiny soldiers.[13] Of course, the British Government had known about Bulls Project Babylon, long before the model was exhibited, as had every intelligence service in the world.

By convening a Parliamentary Select Committee, the Governments idea was to silence speculation and cover-up the truth. The Labour members of the committee however were not so easily manipulated, and later asked me to advise them.

Their own leader Neil Kinnock of course knew about Supergun, but he had done nothing. Now that the affair was subject to scrutiny by a Select Committee, he was off the hook in regards to Super-gun. Still hanging was the rest of the arms sold to Iraq and the 'commissions' and money laundering. Another episode in the saga of my life was beginning.

Douglas Hoyle MP was a leading member of the Trade and industry Select Committee. He was a roly-poly cherub-faced man with

---

[13] Nearly one year after the Bagdad Trade Fair, Trade Secretary Nicholas Ridley told Parliament that the Government had only just become aware of the existence of the supergun project.

a gigantic intellect. However, what made me admire Douglas Hoyle was his integrity. He wanted to make the world a better place; he valued truth and was brave and resourceful.

Today I was driving to Parliament to meet with Doug Hoyle MP, Stan Crowther MP and the other Labour members of the Select Committee.[14] As an advisor on intelligence matters to the Labour members, I was busy arranging meetings. I had agreed to stop off on my way to London to meet with a State Assassin in a venue I had visited once or twice a while back.

Utterly lost I glanced at the multi-colored map nestling close to the Browning on the passenger seat. It did not help. The highway edged with neat, close, red houses, daubed here and there with green splashes was like a Monet landscape. The purr of the engine was reassuring, lost I may be, but I was not going to break down

Arriving at a monstrous donut roundabout I entered with trepidation going round slowly, no that exit was not Telford that was not to Telford, none of them were to Telford, Frustrated and confused I went round again. Looking into the driving mirror, I could see the shadows had drawn close, forced to follow like sheep.

We were a little green, gray and black convoy going round and round. The watcher in the first car, a young man with a shock of pale brown hair, leaned out of the window gesturing towards an upcoming exit. *They are supposed to be keeping me under discrete surveillance not signaling to me.* Never the less I turned, they followed suit, then drew back to a safe and we are not tailing you, distance as I sped along the road towards Telford.

Just a short trek off the main road I turned into the clubs private walled car park. It was empty save for a motorbike huddled under a metal overhang. In the half-open side entrance, a slender young man stood smoking a cigarette.

As I approached him, he trembled, nervous as a puppy caught

---

14 Documentary with Stan Crowther   http://www.cbc.ca/archives/entry/british-parliament-investigates-iraqs-supergun

eating your best shoes. It was clear was waiting for me, as he beckoned me inside with a movement of his troubled eyes.

Following him down a hallway, we arrived at a wood and stained glass barroom door. My escort pushed it open with a silent invitation to step inside.

Darkness wrapped around me as the door clanged shut behind me like a cage. It took a moment before my eyes became accustomed to the absence of sunlight. Slowly the magnificent biscuit colored dance floor came into view. A green-blue carpet snaked around it topped with orange wooden tables and chairs strewn around like autumnal leaves. Vast, empty and exuding the dangerous elegance of an abandoned luxury liner about to sink.

Along the length of the left-hand side mirrored wall, clung a massive black and silver bar. In the middle of which stood, an open quarter bottle of pink Lansom accompanied by a single champagne flute. Perfectly positioned in front was a high bar stool. It was a cute touch, taking my place on the stool; I laughed imagining the curtains opening, the music beginning and the audience appearing to watch the show.

Pouring the golden liquid into the glass, I swept it gracefully aloft, to salute my reflection in the Smokey glass. *'Could it be poisoned'* but I quickly dismissed the thought. Mossad, of course, were expert poisoners. Their scientists created hideous concoctions in suburban Tel Aviv. As far as I knew Ian had not worked for them, and anyway Mossad had a soft spot for me, although I could never make out why.

Doomed to wait, trapped in a terror I just could not feel, I shifted my concentration to the rising champagne bubbles. Only the slow, steady pulse beating in my temples told me I was on edge.

The door behind me swung open, shattering the trance. Silently I cursed myself. *How could I have forgotten my training; always face the entrance.* With studied nonchalance, I turned to face the door. A sudden and brief waterfall of sunlight flooded the darkened room outlining Ian. As abruptly as the light had entered, it retreated when the door closed.

Ian stood stock still, reminding me of a boarhound who had just caught the scent. Fit, wiry and middle-aged, the gray shabby casualness of his clothes was set off by highly polished black shoes. In a burst of activity, he strode over to me with the brisk step of a military man. Pulling up a stool he lounged with one long leg reaching the ground and the other placed on the middle rung of the stool. An indolent pose with a hint of arrogance.

"Hello," he said. "How are you doing?"

There was an undertone of intimidation as if I might not be doing so well.

"Hello Ian. What's happening?"

Tapping the bar with his left-hand fingers, he said, "What's happening is I have received certain information and that information is about you."

I took a slow sip of champagne "Oh yes, what information is that?"

He leaned towards me staring into my eyes as if to push home a feeling I just could not feel.

"You've meddled in things you shouldn't meddle in."

Ignoring the invective, staring straight into his burgeoning pupils I said, "Just following leads. Anyway, I am fully protected."

He shifted away from my gaze.

"Things change," he said, with overt menace.

It reminded me that earlier in the year Gerald Bull had been assassinated and a week later Editor of Defense Helicopter World and erstwhile MI6 agent Jonathan Moyle had been suicided. Gerald James, Chairman of Astra Holdings Defense Company, had said that Stephan Kock and Group 13 were behind the murder of Moyle and Bull:

'… This individual, Stephanus Adolphus Kock had high-level political connections to Thatcher, Heseltine, Younger, Hanley, etc. as well as MI5 and MI6 connections. It is now clear to me that he was involved in the murder of Dr. Gerald Bull in Brussels on 22nd March 1990 and Jonathan Moyle in Santiago,

Chile on 31st March 1990.' [15]

Gerald was a charming man who did not believe women should be involved in arms and intelligence, which was old school but sweet. Gerald James and Bull were working together on a strategy, which would prevent Thatcher and Co taking over Astra, when Bull was assassinated. Bull strode up to the door of his 6th-floor apartment, unaware he was no-longer on the protected list. As he fumbled for his keys, three shots were fired by a silenced 7.65 mm handgun into his back and two more into his head as he slumped. A mere two weeks later parts of Bull's 1000mm Super-gun were 'found' by UK customs. From the moment it was conceived in the brilliant mind of Canadian scientist, Gerald Bull Super-gun was destined to be the precursor unraveling the whole 'Arms to Iraq' saga.

"What about Bull?" I asked, "I'm helping the Select Committee."

"Oh, I know about that," he said.

"Do you mean about Bull, or about the Select Committee?"

"Both," he said.

"The papers are saying it was Mossad or an Iraq hit."

"Mossad was watching they were stationed over the road."

"So it wasn't Mossad?"

"No, they only had a watching brief."

"That coincides with my thoughts; after all, they would need authorization from UK PLC and the Americans to take out Bull. Johnathan Moyle, however, that looks right up your street."

"You ask too many questions."

Would I end up like Jonathan Moyle, discovered hanging in the wardrobe of room 406 in the Hotel Carrera, Chile with a pillowcase shoved over his head. Jonathan was copybook suicided ending his investigations in Chile.

---

[15] Gerald James In the Public Interest: Little, Brown & Company; Revised edition (December 15, 1995) **ISBN-13:** 978-0316877190

He was looking into Allivane International, ISC and Chilean Arms dealer Carlos Cardoon's friendship with Mark Thatcher, the UK Prime Minister's son.

Allivane was set-up as a cross Atlantic, arms embargo breaking front company by Margaret Thatcher, MI6 and the CIA, with Cardoen as a key figure. International Signal and control Corp (ISC) was supplying via Cardoen, cluster-bomb technology and blueprints to build a cluster-bomb factory all with the help of the Thatcher Government. [16]

Following the bizarre death of Jonathan Moyle who was drugged and suffocated before being strung up in the wardrobe, the Foreign Office began a discrediting campaign. They spread rumors that Jonathan had killed himself in a bizarre sex game. Tony Moyle, Jonathan's father and I often spoke on the phone. Tony was attempting to come to terms with the destruction of his worldview, shattered by the murder of his son and the contrived discrediting operation set in motion by the British Government. Johnathan's mother had spoken with her son less than half an hour before he died:

'I spoke to Jonathan ten minutes before he probably died and he complained his room had been ransacked.'

Ian's eyes were boring into me as if he was reading my thoughts. They would know I was talking with Tony Moyle.

"Things change," Ian repeated, "you should watch your step."

The pattern of the bizarre was a trademark of a group of 'State sanctioned assassins and spotters' to which Ian belonged. Having obtained authorization for the hit they would sit down with their handlers and plan the bizarre details of their targets murder. If the assassination was urgent, they would just gun them down with stunning professionalism, while the spotters covered for them.

Ian shifted on the stool, saying, "And a lonely walk by the lake."

---

[16] The illegal trade in death would have repercussions down the decades. In 2017 it was reported that British Cluster Bombs sold during the Thatcher era were being used by Saudi Arabia to bomb the innocent people of Yemen.

In his unique way, he was imparting information about Shani Warren.

Lifting my eyes, I stared into his for a moment.

"The lady of the lake?"

His eyes narrowed and he drifted into memories, I could almost see the young woman pleading for her life.

Pretty 26-year-old Shani Warren, was dubbed the Lady of the Lake and listed as one of the twenty-five 1980's suspicious Marconi Deaths. It was the era of Ronni Regan's' Stars Wars program and Marconi was working on the top-secret Star Wars technology. Although the young engineers were more interested in finding out about Marconi's use of the latest space tech techniques to build carbon fiber chassis for F1 racing cars. However, Shani Warren was not a scientist or an engineer; she was a secretary in a company acquired by GEC Marconi.

I took a sip from the glass glancing at Ian's face through the bubbles; he seemed to struggle with an inner demon.

Shani Warren was over-the-moon she had just made the final payment on her new Black Vauxhall Cavalier. That evening she was going to have an intimate celebration with her boyfriend. In the afternoon, she mowed her lawn in Stoke Poges, Buckinghamshire, placing the cuttings into plastic bags. Happy and excited Shani pushed the bags into the boot of her new car so she could dump them later. Then drove to purchase supplies for the celebration.

Women love flowers and Shani was no exception, she purchased a huge bouquet of dancing red, white, and blue blooms to adorn her lounge, and a bottle of champagne to crack open for a toast. In anticipation, the flowers and champagne nestled together on the back seat of her car.

Her planned celebration did not take place. Tied up like a dead chicken Shani drowned in Lake Taplow. Surrounding the lake were the houses of some of London's top Judges and celebrities such as Ernie Wise, Terry Wogan, Frank Bough and Michael Parkinson. They could easily have looked across the lake as Shani took her last breath.

Had she driven to the lake on her own, been lured there or driven there? Were they waiting for her in some lonely lane to surprise her? No mention of a struggle was made by the Police. Professional killers have access to secret, sophisticated untraceable drugs; none of their victims seemed to struggle. Interested as I was in the procedure, I knew it would be a mistake to ask Ian.

Nearby Shani's lifeless body, Police found the contents of her car strewn over the grass as if someone had ravaged through the car searching for something. Her handbag was missing, and the keys to her car were never found. Police removed the flowers and champagne. It was discovered that her brand new car had a serious fault in the gearbox, making it difficult to drive. Someone had deliberately damaged the gearbox. ITN reported that:

> 'Her body showed no sign of injury & police say they can't rule out the possibility of a bizarre suicide.'

Notwithstanding the evidence, the Police version was that Shani placed a noose around her neck, gagged herself with a blue scarf, tied her feet with a rope and tied her hands behind her back with spark plug leads. Stumbled in high heels to the edge of Lake Taplow where she threw herself down into 18inches of water to drown herself in a slow and excruciatingly painful way. The Home Office Pathologist Dr. Ben Davies agreed with the Police it was suicide.

As time went on and Shani's death became notorious and Police needed to put a stop to speculation. A series of rapes with a common theme had taken place in Leeds, Bradford, Leister and Nottingham. All the victims were abducted from city center car parks. Geographical-profiling expert Colin Johnson was called in. Johnson's expertise led to the arrest of serial rapist Clive Barwell from Leeds in Yorkshire. [17]

Shani was way outside Barwell's geographical area, living 204 miles away. However, it was an opportunity not to be missed by the Police who informed the press they were questioning Barwell about Shani. Barwell was charged with and admitted three rapes, one attempted murder and four kidnappings, one serious sexual assault, one indecent assault and one assault causing actual bodily harm

---

[17]   Geographical profiling expert catches Barwell
http://www.wired.co.uk/article/mapping-murder
http://news.bbc.co.uk/2/hi/uk_news/464844.stm

The judge Mr. Justice Penry-Davey at Teesside Crown Court ordered three other charges to lie on file, a kidnapping and rape in Leicester in 1984, and an attempted kidnapping in Leeds in 1993. Barwell refused to bow to police pressure making it clear he did not attack Shani Warren. Despite this, the Police, having failed to have Shani's death accepted as suicide, decided to blame her death on Barwell.

Was Shani's real murderer sitting next to me in the empty barroom one leg almost touching mine? I could do nothing with the knowledge. He knew he was untouchable. Surgically he was using the information to frighten me into silence. I knew that if he was authorized to kill me we would not be having this conversation. It was just a polite warning.

"Why was Shani taken out, she was just a secretary?"

He walked around the bar to pour himself a pint.

"Secretaries get to know too much."

I watched as the frothy larger spilled over the sides of the dimpled beer glass falling into the sink.

"It's the Salami effect," he said.

"Is that the reason for the Marconi deaths?

"Slices of Salami," he said sneering.

Marconi operated a cell-like structure. Within the cell, the lowest secretary to the highest manager knew everything about the project they were working on. It was hinted that this cell structure was part and parcel of the strange list of deaths. In hushed tones, those in the know also mentioned Star Wars and reverse engineering.

Tom was a young engineer working on star wars when we met. "Assassins are being drafted in from other government projects to take care of problems as they come up," he said, his auburn hair flopping into his green eyes, "I am not worried for myself being an insider, but it's a troubling development."

"Yes, it looks, as if they are being suicided to order," I agreed. Those suicided to order knew too much were expendable and their usefulness was outranked by their danger to Marconi's paymasters.

In each case just hours after the death, grey suited men arrived to collect what they described as defence documents from the grief-stricken families. Doug Hoyle MP who I was traveling to London to meet had called for the Government to look into the deaths and find out why Police stopped their investigations. He had said:

"Something sinister is at work."

Of course, Doug was right and he knew it, but in the world of politics if you do not tread carefully you will be their next victim. Was this a reason Ian had mentioned the Lady in the Lake?

"How did you get into this line of business Ian?"

"Angola, the bastards fucked us over."

He came back to the bar almost slamming the beer glass onto the top so that the head rocked sending little frothy rivulets onto the beer mat below.

"Angola," he repeated a scowl deepening across his brow.

You need a particularly psychopathic personality to carry out such cold-blooded and harrowing murders. Which is the reason assassins are recruited, willingly or by coercion, from the dregs of failed wars and coups. Ex-soldiers with a particular bent for raping and murdering children and a sick lust for torture. These psychopaths fit neatly into the slots left open by the controlling psychopaths who run the United Kingdom.

"What happened in Angola?" I asked him.

"We were in mufti, but we were British soldiers. When it went wrong, we were treated like mercenaries. We were abandoned."

"But some were mercenaries weren't they?"

"Yes, some were, but it was coordinated by six. Bastards." Ian shook his head, "We were let down."

With these duplicitous people, you did not know what was truth and what were half-truths. The Civil war in Angola had spawned a strange mix of mercenaries and professionals and spies mixed up in a civil war. Later named the dogs of war a motley crew of soldiers of fortune, MI6 officers, ex SAS, SBS Para's, Foreign Legionnaires,

Rhodesian SAS and Green Jackets with some pilots thrown in.[18]

It all went wrong for the dogs of war when they were arrested and prosecuted. Three were sentenced to death and others given long prison sentences. Prime Minister James Callahan, former Mr fix-it for dissolute MP's who would later be implicated in the Bank of Credit and Commerce (BCCI) scandal, had asked for the return of his dogs of war without success.

Taking another sip from the glass, I asked, "What about Darren?"

"He was there too," he said.

Darren owned a business in town whose extracurricular activity was selling illegal pornographic films. His specialty was child pornography, including snuff movies where a child would be raped, tortured and murdered on video. These were highly prized and highly priced, but he did not sell them he hired them all out under the protection of the local North Wales Police who were also his customers and suppliers. Children in local children's homes were being used to supplement his collection.

"What do you know about the kids Darren?"

"Now that's your problem you ask too many questions."

Was it my interference with the child abuse image trade and police corruption they were complaining about. Was I, in their terms, being politely warned to stop meddling.

In the nineties North Wales was a hotbed of Welsh Nationalists giving the North Wales Police anti-terrorist squad a reason to control the Borders of the Principality? They arranged small explosions blaming them on Welsh Nationalists. They protected drug traffickers, government terrorists from Ireland and contraband coming in via Holy-Head port. Freelance drug dealers were ruthlessly eliminated with their drugs confiscated and sent back on the streets through authorized channels.

It all worked neatly and the Media had little interest in what

---

[18] http://www.mercenary-wars.net/angola/

happened above the Watford Gap. All of this, which may have seemed a far cry from illegal arms sales, but it, was actually interwoven. A criminal mafia of great sophistication masquerading as governments and security was taking over control step by step as they elevated their pedophile politicians into top positions.

"So do you know who killed Bull?" I asked.

"Oh yes, I know."

"I am told Kock was behind it."

"That's a Kock and Bull story," he chortled. "You do poke your nose in where it's not wanted don't you."

Putting down his beer glass, he leaned towards me.

"Do you have a back door?"

"Why?" I asked.

"You will need a back door," he said standing up.

Ian's insistence on a back door while a warning was almost helpful. Yes, I may need an escape plan. Would the fake passport I had been issued with serve to get me out or should I get an identity they knew nothing about, I made a mental note to keep a case packed.

We parted with a nod as he retraced his steps back to the sparkling door and was gone, leaving me to my turbulent inner thoughts. I still had a long journey ahead of me and needed to evaluate if I had gleaned anything from this meeting. Hopping off the bar stool, I walked to the sparkling door Ian had passed through, opened it and stepped out.

The neon sunlight drove away all the spectral reflections. With death as an advisor on my shoulder, I resumed the journey to London, to meet Doug Hoyle MP and Stan Crowther MP.

12. DEADLY GAME

"It is to be regretted that the rich and powerful too often bend the acts of government to their own selfish purposes." Andrew Jackson

The police descended on my cottage like a swarm of black locusts at seven in the morning. They proceeded to search my two houses, three-quarters of acre gardens and ample outbuildings for evidence of the murder of the elderly woman, Mrs. Edna Simms, from next door. Outside a Huge black windowless Police van stood at the cottage gate, from which fifteen uniformed officers had tumbled out to begin their pointless search.

One wraith like the officer stormed into my home without a search warrant and now stood guarding the door, from the Dining room to the yard as if I might try to make a run for it. The dining room windows overlooked the yard and the red painted gate with the black police van outside. Ignoring him for the moment, I sat on a two-century's old plain wooden chair, gazing at the comforting gleam of the old black Aga, a piece of sanity in the otherwise crazy world.

The wraith in his flat blue cap shifted nervously from one foot to another. A lackey of an elite corrupt and criminal ruling class paid to perform his duties perfunctorily, paid to act not to think.

Of course, the search of my property was intimidation and a step towards the removal of a thorn in their side. In a topsy-turvy world where truth is a lie, I could not be permitted to walk the earth freely espousing truth. It was to them unthinkable that I would be allowed to threaten their organized criminal enterprises. I was spending a lot of time in London with the Labour Members of the Select Committee unearthing Tory politician's arms gravy train. Perhaps even worse in their eyes, I continued to investigate the Westminster pedophile ring and the exploitation of disadvantaged kids from children's homes

Seventy-eight-year-old Mrs. Simms had disappeared on Boxing Day, that same day my house was also ransacked. *Had she stumbled upon them?* The Police had organized a fake search with a roadblock nearby, stopping motorists to ask if they had seen the old woman.

The wraith officer's presence in the dining room was a malignant force, a darkness that somehow tarnished the pristine cleanliness of the quarry-tiled floor.

Looking up at this shadow of a being, "what are you looking for, if I may ask?"

His mouth opened, but before he could utter a word, the door behind swung open. Tornado-like, the burly form of a special branch officer (SB), entered with a second even fatter SB officer in tow behind him. The wraith, shrank as he recognized the SB officer who acknowledged his presence with a dismissive toss of his head towards the door. Dutifully the wraith slunk out like a rat caught stealing a chunk of bread.

Without a word, they both deposited themselves on the farmhouse sofa in front of me, their bulk taking up almost every square inch. The sound of retreating steps moving across the yard outside echoed through the windows. We waited in silence until the last uniformed officer climbed into the big black van and the engine fired.

"I thought we were on the same side," said the senior officer, whom I knew as Henry, but it was not his real name.

"So did I."

Were we talking about the impending war in the Gulf and the vast profits, politicians made from selling illegal arms to Iraq. Allied troops were to be sent into Iraq to face weapons supplied by their own Governments; this had led to a rift in the Intelligence Community. Alternatively, were they talking about VIP's and the abuse of vulnerable kids from children's homes?

Just one month earlier Frank Beck, a former Children's Home

Manager in Leicester had received five life sentences for child abuse. The Judge made sure Beck stayed in jail for life where he could be prevented spilling the beans about the Westminster pedophile ring.

The two police detectives involved in the Beck case Kelvyn Ashby and Mick Creedon were on my list. They had been brought in to cover-up for MP, Lord Greville Janner QC, a significant member of the Westminster Pedophiles. Ashby and Creedon were accused of disappearing evidence and silencing victims by threatening them with prosecution. All to protect Janner and his co-conspirators who were guilty of a catalog of crimes against children.

Special Branch worked with police officers like Ashby and Creedon, cops who helped them with cover-ups, dodgy intelligence gathering and evidence disappearing.

"We have ordered the wooden-tops out," Henry said, fixing me with a hard stare and ending, "this can stop here."

Perhaps it was both the arms and the kids. Without telepathy, it was impossible to know exactly what we were talking about, but I understood he meant my imminent arrest and set-up for the murder of Mrs. Simms would not take place if I played ball.

I looked at them and they looked back at me across the antique red clay tiled uneven floor; we were all testing the ground. They were both Freemasons and the shadow of a dark god hung over them. These were levels I could walk in, grasp the power and win this contest.

I had a feeling the bulky silent one, whose aura was so dark it cast a shadow on the white wall behind him, would have preferred to strangle me.

Some awareness beyond my consciousness watched this silent opera with dispassion. Rising above I looked down, travelled into their feelings, and saw they had murdered Edna Simms.

This conversation was not about weapons or war in the gulf, not about the stolen children it was about those who stood behind me.

They were servants of a hidden evil power and I could not bring myself to play games with them. As fellow occultists, they saw my resolve and the dance was over without another word. Standing up, they left without a backward glance and I watched them walk across the yard and out of the red painted metal gate and disappear from my life. They may have dismissed the uniformed officers (wooden tops), but it was not over.

Without time to gather my fragmented thoughts, another knock at the door sent me spinning. Two plainclothes detectives were at the dining room door inviting me to come 'voluntarily' to the Police Station in Bangor. The Voluntary part meant I could drive myself shadowed by the two unmarked police vehicles, which now stood in the lane.

I picked up the keys to the Ford Orion Ghia 1.6I which was a nippy little saloon I had just purchased from a fellow dealer. Using driving skills I overtook the car ahead zooming away, they struggled to follow me and the three-mile journey from Rhyd-y Groes to the Police Station in Bangor was over in a flash. I parked in the police compound along with the two unmarked police cars; the detectives escorted me into the Station.

Chief Inspector Gareth Luke sat at his large brown desk strewn with papers in piles across the surface like sad orphans in little heaps.

The large, unruly gray haired head looked up as I was brought in.

Leaning back in his executive chair with a studied nonchalance.

"Sit down." He indicated to a wooden chair in front of his desk.

"If you drive like that you will save us the trouble..." he said, letting the sentence drop.

"Your men need training in the driving skills area."

"Your driving is a skill, then?" he said, moving his bulk to face me. "Who do you work for?"

It was a typical early interrogation ploy. Arrested, brought to a strange room, placed on a small chair in front of an enormous desk with questions thrown at you. I had read the manual and seen the movies. I remained silent.

"I know Clive..." he paused. "And I know his wife."

It was a barb. I raised my eyes to his small, set too close and watery eyes.

"Are you SAS?" he yelled.

Remaining silent, I stared into his eyes. Desert Storm was in full swing and I was involved in missions behind enemy lines, with flights going from RAF Valley in Anglesey. *Did he know.*

"Who do you work for?" he repeated.

"You're not cleared to know Gareth; you're just a policeman."

He starred at me with loathing, his ill temper hard to control, but I could see he was aware the interrogation was going get him nowhere.

"Well, we will see," he said, turning as if to inspect some papers on his desk.

"You can go for now," he said without looking up.

Leisurely stood up and walked out of his office door. A detective escorted me to the police station car park, then left, closing the door behind him.

With the tension gone, I went through my training like a kaleidoscope of memories spinning in and out focus until they stopped and formed into a pattern with a strange clarity. Oh yes, there were those strange things I did not remember learning. Climbing into my car I turned over the engine, there was no need to check underneath for bombs, as they would not want to blow up their police station.

The dark shadow of the mountaintops cast a strange gloom over the land as I drove along the snakelike country road wending my solitary way back home. Thoughts were tumbling around my head like lottery balls; I needed to contact Clive.

As I drove, I watched the lonely roads; there were few cars, so it was easy to monitor for surveillance, the police were not tailing me. Passing a telephone box, I slowed down and stopped; no one was behind me. I continued to the next shiny red phone box which stood on the long empty road from Llanberis to the Seiont roundabout. It was always more difficult for them to tap a conversation from a telephone box they did not know would be used. For this reason, I never used the same box twice for that very reason. After scanning up and down the deserted road, I entered the phone box and dialed.

"Customs Holyhead."

"Put me through to Clive Menzies please."

"Who shall I say is calling?"

"It's Sara."

The girl who I had not met was accustomed to fielding calls and she knew the name I used.

"Please wait a moment."

The seconds ticked by

"Hello Tara," a familiar voice gave me a rush of warmth and security.

"We need to meet Clive."

"Yes," he said, "Go home, I will call you with a time and place, be ready."

"Okay." I said, replacing the black plastic public receiver on its cradle.

Arriving back, the familiar red metal gate, gleaming in the cold winter sun, welcomed me. Rushing to the door, I opened it, then closed it hard shut behind me. Breathing a sigh of relief, I leaned against it; all I wanted was to sit down with a cup of tea in my own home without the Stormtroopers.

Picking up the kettle, I placed it on its white plastic heating pad. It was all so familiar, simple and comforting. I grabbed the Port Merion jar labeled TEA in big black bold letters and placed a tea bag in a mug. As I stood gazing out of the Kitchen window, listening for the hiss of boiling water, I heard the sound of a car drawing up outside. *What now?*

The clanging sound of the gate opening focused me. I went back into the dining room to see Chief Inspector Gareth Luke with one uniformed officer and two plainclothes detectives in tow crossing the yard.

Opening the door, Luke pushed a search warrant into my hand as two uniformed officers pushed past me and began trawling through the house turning out draws and rifling in the cupboards.

"We're seizing the Ford and taking it to forensics?" Luke said.

"Seizing my Orion," I said. "Why?"

"We will find blood and hair in the boot," he said with certainty.

"Only if you put them there," I replied.

"So tell me what do you think happened?"

"Mrs. Simms discovered 'them' illegally entering my house and they took her out."

"No, they are real professionals."

One of the officers arrived with my credit cards in several different names and Leya's which she had left with me for safe keeping. He handed them to Luke.

"Oh look at this," he said, rifling through the cards. "Leya Morrison, did you steal this?"

"No, she left it with me for safekeeping so that she would not use it," I said, "ask her if you want."

"Oh, we will," he said, placing them in an evidence bag.

"Just sit down there," he said, pointing to the farmhouse sofa.

We waited in silence as the detectives came in and out carrying boxes of property.

As they removed the final box, Luke said with menace, "We are going now, but we will be back after examining the evidence."

Walking through the lounge, I noticed the tiny model of an e-type jaguar was missing from the window ledge. From the office, computers, camera, expensive lenses all gone. Papers they did not want lay strewn over the carpet.

Climbing the flight of extremely steep stairs to the upstairs floor, I went to the bedroom. The antique draws were open; their contents strewn over the floor. The white canopied double bed left covered in clothes from the wardrobe, colored silks, browns, green, scarlets, purples and indigos lying sprawled in heaps as if a bad-tempered child had thrown them onto her bed in a hysterical fit. Shoes, belts and hats littered the carpeted floor. The jewelry box my mother gave to me was empty, every gold chain, broach, gold ring, my grandmother's cameo taken. *I am being violated by the State to shut me up, to close me down.*

Walking through the debris of my property, I slumped down onto the window seat, giving the white satin cushion, embroidered with roses by my mother, a soft stroke. Looking out over the huge lawn towards Caernarvon I considered the history of the house. It started life over 500 years ago, its walls were 3 feet 6 inches thick and it was rumored to be the Inn where the bishop of York had met Prince Llewelyn in secret.

Just above my head, a priest-hole still existed connected by a secret staircase, leading from the inglenook fire downstairs up into the roof. Sometime in the last few hundred years, it was filled in with rubble for a reason I could not guess. The house had seen injustice and persecution before, Had a priest hidden in fear above my head while Henry the Eighth's troops paraded up and down the country lanes looking for Catholic priests to drag out, lasso behind their horses to drag them bloody before a crowd of frightened people and murder them. Did the priest and his protectors feel the same hunted fear I felt?

As the years ground on, the Robber Barons had torn our children from us, transporting them to Australia for use as sex slaves. Promoting their agenda of removing children from their families and their ancient heritage until no remnant of honor or self-worth remained. Indoctrinating them into a culture without honor, which serves the robber barons crown of England and a legal system designed to crush them.

All these genetic memories tumbled from the roof as I gazed over the quiet landscape waiting. The phone on the bedside table rang out I picked up the crème receiver.

"Hallo."

"Meet me in Newborough at 17.30 hrs," Clive said, before the phone went dead.

Below me, the peacock let out a howl of rage as he sparred with next doors cockerel.

"Krishna no fighting with the cockerel," I yelled, out of the window.

They both moved out of sight, behind the tumbledown building, which had once been pigsties.

Although a misty winter sun hung in the sky, casting a clear light onto every leaf and stem in the garden. Patches of sunlight clung to the damp grass on the lawn and the scent of earth not long since crushed by ice crawled up to my open window.

Was it still only four, what a day. The adrenaline was still pumping through my veins and the drive would take me three-quarters of an hour. *What should I wear?* It was January and deathly cold and the meet was close to the sea. Rummaging amongst the abandoned clothes on the bed, I picked out a brown knitted asymmetrical woolen skirt adorned with satin ribbons and jacket to match with a big red satin droopy flower on the left-hand side. A beige, cashmere, roll neck sweater picked up from the floor where the police had left it and long brown boots finished the ensemble. Amongst the scattered remnants of my property, I gave a twirl before the full-length mirror. When a girl is well dressed, she can face anything.

Tripping downstairs, I went to the Daimler, retrieved the keys from the sun visor and drove out of the red gates. Making my way to the Isle of Anglesey, over the graceful Menai suspension bridge built by Thomas Telford, I took the coast road to Newborough Forest, which covered seven hundred hectares. Tall Corsican pines climbed to the skies interspersed with native trees, night- black-winged ravens croaked as red squirrels who scurried unseen high in the branches with a background sound of crashing waves beyond the dunes.

Few people lived near the forest and I saw almost no non-involved vehicles. The 'meet' was monitored and kept secure by agents in vehicles who let me know with a smile or a nod that I was safe and the pathway was being kept clear. At the entrance to the beach road, an agent in a lorry had parked. The road down was long and steep; twisting between huge pines and banks of sand. To stop the car hurtling to the bottom I kept my foot on the brakes.

At the base two large car parks stood almost empty, turning I saw Clive standing at the front end of his big black vehicle I drove up and parked next to him. Opening the door with a soft click. The chill salt-laden air surrounded me; it was a wild place in January half-frozen and hostile only the towering dunes of sand provided shelter from the roving sea winds. I could hear the crashing of waves against the shore on the other side of the Dunes as I walked over to him.

A big strong muscular man formerly SAS he now masqueraded as a customs officer. Clive was the most admirable man I have ever met in my life. Built like a rock he was as gentle as a dove with an unflappable manner, which housed a razor-sharp mind and lightning reactions.

Rushing to him, his arms encircled me and the warmth of his chest oozed out chasing away the cold. It was like hugging a grizzly bear I could not reach around his chest.

"Hello, Tara," he said.

"Hello, Clive."

"Let's sit in the car," he said, going round to his driver seat and getting in while I slid onto the passenger seat

"What are the Police up to?"

"They are trying to set me up for the Murder of my next door neighbor's mother, Mrs. Simms."

"That's a poor interrogation technique," he said.

I looked at his calm face, poor interrogation technique, murdering an old lady and trying to set someone up for it seemed extreme.

"They raided my house, they seized my car."

"What did they ask you?"

"Who I worked for, and he mentioned you by name Clive."

"Okay."

"They think I am in SAS."

"Well, we have women as you know."

"Tara, go home, I will deal with this. Some people owe me favors."

His hand reached out and lingered on mine for a moment.

"Go home. You will be safe," he said.

"I'm sorry, I made a mistake," I said, sliding off the seat through the open car door.

"There are no mistakes, only things that happen," he said, as I stood buffeted by the sea breeze with one of the most admirable men.

When I arrived back home, the phone was ringing as I opened the door. I picked up but said nothing.

"It's Chief Inspector Luke."

"Yes."

"I want to apologize; your car will be returned. It was a misunderstanding."

"Yes, it was," I said.

"We will return everything tomorrow."

"What time?"

"In the morning, around 10am."

"Okay." I agreed replacing the receiver.

Upstairs I kicked off my boots, lay down on the disheveled bed and went to sleep. It had been a long day.

The next morning the Police arrived with the Ford Orion and boxes of property. I watched them as they brought in box after box, placing them in a heap in the dining room.

Opening one, I found it all packaged and sealed in numbered incident bags. The computers appeared and the camera. Looking through the boxes, the telephoto lens and jewelry were missing

"Where is my jewelry and telephoto lens?"

"Sorry, we've mislaid them, but we are looking for them," the Detective said, depositing the keys to Orion on the kitchen table.

"Well, please bring them back as soon as possible," I said to their retreating backs.

Picking up the Orion's keys, I went out to check it. Opening the door a strong smell of cleaning fluid hit me. The car was spotless. They had cleaned every fragment of hair and blood from the carpets.

No evidence remained of the murder. [19]

---

[19]　Three months later in March 1991 Mrs. Simms decomposed body was discovered up a very steep mountain track not far from where she had disappeared.

13. KOCK AND BULL STORY

"And remember, where you have a concentration of power in a few hands, all too frequently men with the mentality of gangsters get control. History has proven that." Lord Acton

The train drew shunting and hissing into Glasgow Central Station. Emerging through the carriage window, appeared a vision of Victorian wrought iron grandeur, peopled with mindless shuffling passengers all wanting to be somewhere else. Snatching up my overnight bag, I jostled to descend onto the platform, which had witnessed the passing of a million feet. My meeting with Frank Machon, Allivane's arms deliver and organization spook occupied my thoughts, as I headed for the exit.

Stepping through the arched station portal the driving rain hit me. Drops splattered angrily on the pavement echoing with menace against the stark, dirty grey stone walls. It was the sort of rain, which seeps into your bones, leaving you struggling to get warm again. Through the curtain of unremitting water, I could just make out the stubby form of a black cab, an unctuous shine mottling its bodywork.

The driver flung open the rear door with a creak, which tore through the sound of the rain. To reveal, an empty back seat. In fascination, I watched as the driver's hand snaked back over the front seat to rest on the steering wheel. The gesture was both welcoming and troubling.

If I entered the cab, would I be found suicided like Willie MacRae, on some

desolate rain swept highland moor? A furious burst of rain plastering wet hair to my scalp made up my mind for me. Quickly I shuffled onto the sticky black plastic. The driver did not speak, but I muttered the destination anyway.

We drove through the Gorbals tenements, crammed with twisted humanity struggling to survive amongst the unremitting hatred and contempt of their fellow men. Grubby windows concealed villainous and grotesque secrets; I had stepped back into a Victorian drama holding grim reminders of some dark hidden corner in my subconscious.

The black cab took an indirect route to Franks Warehouse, *Was the diversion intended to conjure up thoughts of Thompson, Knight and Britain's duplicitous arms trafficking to the UDA, IRA and now to Iraq.* Images pushed their way into my mind of Arthur Thompson MI5 run Glasgow gangster and Britain's biggest heroin trafficker.

Supported by agencies of the British State Thompson ruled Glasgow's underworld by violence, fear and intimidation. Running arms to both the Ulster Defense Association (UDA) and the Irish Republican Army (IRA) Thompson could arrange a murder on request.

He worked with his English gangster counterparts the Knights. But also the Krays who were child traffickers to the wealthy and powerful. Thompson's close friend Ronnie Knight had lived a stone's throw from me in Wheathampstead. I remembered dancing in his woodblock ballroom and gathering roses from the huge rose garden.[20]

Of course, the Police and MI5 have the coziest of relationships seconding officers between each other. This muddied all lines between civil and political police enabling the State to use the civil police to target their real or perceived political or business threats. It also allowed them to protect organized criminal agents, like Thompson.

---

[20] Gotcha John Knight, Peter Wilton, Pete Sawyer Ronnie Knight Published 2001 Sidgwick & Jackson ASIN: B001IPRZ22 My colleague and friend Pete Sawyer later wrote the book 'Gotcha' with the Knights and Peter Wilton ex-flying squad officer. Ronnie and Pete presented a signed hardcopy copy with a note of thanks on the flyleaf since seized by police.

While Special Branch, a law unto themselves run by top politicians arranged the murder of political targets like Pat Finucane, [21] a Human Rights Lawyer in Belfast and Willie MacRae, a leading Lawyer and Scottish National Party (SNP) Politician in Glasgow.

Arriving at Franks Warehouse the door was open. On the ground floor, an enormous Iranian Gunboat sprawled, incongruous, so far from Iran and the sea. Sidling past its hull, I climbed the utility iron grate steps, my footfalls making metallic echoes, which bounced rhythmically off the walls. Arms dealers, Civil Servants, Journalists, Intelligence officers and agents from both sides of the pond had climbed these steps before me leaving a faint aura of their presence.

Frank sat waiting behind a massive wooden desk, which overshadowed his slight, wiry build. A starved Greyhound, matchstick body, undulating with hidden strength, topped by a face deeply grooved by the constant stress of vigilance.

As I stepped through the doorway, he nodded to a vacant chair.

"You knew it was me," I said, sitting down in the unadorned old spindle chair.

"Aye, ya shouldnae Ave taken a black cab," he was letting me know black cabs were a useful intelligence source.

"I'm helping the Trade and Industry select committee."

Leaning back into his big old chair, "Aye, I know."

"Your knowledge of Supergun and the deliveries would make a big difference to them," I said.

"Aye it would, but it all for naught, with Bull gone and Kock camped in Astra."

Shuffling on the rickety chair, I asked, "Was Kock behind the job on Bull?"

---

[21]   Pat Finucane http://www.belfasttelegraph.co.uk/opinion/news-analysis/how-special-branch-betrayed-the-police-34855866.html

"Kocks a rats arse alright. Younger's up there at RBS he told me to deliver this and deliver that and now he says he dos nay know me," shaking his head, "does nay know me, bastards the lot of them, one day I'll be getting on me US Battleship and be gone."

"Kock and Younger know each other, don't they?"

Shifting his body to an upright position, "Aye they do an Kocks no far from ere, up in Oban. Been brought in, safe pair of 'ands to clear the deck."

"So Bull was done for when he was going to spill the beans?"

Glancing at the black telephone on the desk, "The call was made," he said.

"Bull warned Chris Gumbly they were all being set-up, an hour later he was shot." [22]

"Bull was bright, but no bright enough, the meeting he had wi Grumbly and his lawyers was no secret."

"So the Government took him out?"

Looking at me with a sideways glance, he said, "Aye, that's how it works."

"What about the propellant for Project Babylon you delivered to Asil Nadirs, Unipac in Cyprus?"

"That was a chocolate egg," he laughed.

"What about you Frank, will they go for you?"

---

[22] http://shellnews.net/PDFs/GeraldJamesStatement1June2007.pdf 'I met Bull in November 1989, and he warned me of the fact that we would be set up, of serious corruption and of the fact that he intended to do something about it. He also told me of current cooperation with PRB and BMARC re Iraq. He approached us again in March 1990 through our Austrian agent, Cranz, and Chris Gumbley. He met Gumbley on 22nd March 1990 for a whole day with Cranz and his lawyers and told him he wanted me to return the next week with documents to help his case against HMG and senior civil servants, which he had already launched. Bull was particularly concerned about corruption and the fact he had offered more for PRB than Astra. He also seemed to know we would all be set up. An hour after Gumbley left him he was shot.'

His face crumpled with inner anger, Frank would not make a Poker Player.

"Lots of them know a wee bit, but I can put it together, that's what makes me powerful and dangerous."

He glared at some unknown spectral image, may be of George Younger or Stephan Kock or Margaret Thatcher or maybe some inner demon within his mind.

"Dangerous?"

He ruffled a stack of papers on the desk, "An' I've twelve thousand documents to prove it."

Frank sat fluffed up like the Goose on the golden egg atop a nest of fake end-user certificates, lists of arms delivered to whom and from whom, drawings, letters, the ins and outs. Franks photographic memory recalled every document and every figure. He was a goldmine of information, but it was a Herculean task to tie him down to answer your questions. Every so often, he would thrust a document at me to prove a point, let me read it and snatch it back. More rarely, with reluctance, he let me keep a copy.

Frank and his handlers had arranged the delivery of countless shipments of illegal arms to Iraq.[23] Arms were delivered and deals struck, kickbacks arranged to a bevy of corrupt politicians and civil servants while copies of the paperwork were copied and hoarded. The stack of incriminating documents would discredit Governments, Prime ministers and Presidents. It would ruin the careers of the corrupt and save scapegoats involved in the illegal trade conducted with Government sanction.

Making a sweeping gesture with his hands over the desk, "Aye, you can always rely on their arrogance, they put 'em up at the top and they think they're really something. Any Prime Minister, any President can be brought down with the stroke of a pen," he glared at me, "a stroke of a pen."

"I can think of some I would like to, write out, of history," I said.

---

[23] Spiders Web   Alan Friedman, Bantam, Published 1993 ISBN-10: 0553096508

"Love Horse eat grass."

It was one of his weird sayings, horse a colloquialism for heroin and grass for cannabis reminding me of his compatriot Arthur Thompson.

The next day Frank, later to be dubbed super-spook, agreed to fly with me to London to meet Doug Hoyle MP. Walking up the aircraft aisle to our seats, Frank nodded at a black suited twenty-something vulture with a deadpan white face.

"It's the crown," he whispered.

Aware of the young deaths head figure stationed just a few rows behind us; I settled into the window seat my thoughts turning to the unsolved death of Willie MacRae.

"How does the crown fit with the death of Willie MacRae?" Tapping his boney leg with his skeletal hand, "Crowns a straightjacket for the good and the sane, he should nay have messed with George Younger and the like. It wus bound to happen."

Unable to take my eyes from the protruding bone under the black cloth at his knee, "Police say Willie was depressed and terrified of going to jail, because of a drink-driving charge so shot himself with his Antique revolver in his right temple."

Frank leaned forward to pull his seat belt from under his arse.

"That's rubbish; he was no daft, antique revolvers aren't reliable, 22 caliber's more likely to injure than kill ya he a' known that being a pro. An would nay shoot hisseff in the temple instead of through the mouth, or the rear base of is head? It's rubbish."

Without any plausibility, the Police story went like this. Willie had set off from Glasgow to drive to his holiday home in Dornie, drinking Scotch on the way.

During daylight hours, his mechanically sound Volvo had careered off the road near Invergarry rolling down a boggy embankment. The car righted itself, but with damage to the rear windscreen and driver's side window, buckling to the bonnet and roof plus a deflated offside rear tire. Willie, who was not wearing a seatbelt remained seated, took out his illegally owned antique .22 short rim fire revolver, chambered a bullet, pulled back the firing pin, placed the barrel next to his right temple and shot himself.

Two days later, he died of his injury. An Autopsy did not test for alcohol and Police did not conduct a forensic examination of the weapon. The valuable numbered antique collector's revolvers circa 1868-75, together with some important documents were 'lost' by the Police.

"Police are talking nonsense as usual," I said, "he was on his way to his holiday home in Dornie and -"

"Seven miles from Dornie, SAS and 'Six' were training the mujahedeen over the water from Kylie of Lochalsh on the Applecross peninsula in demolition, reconnaissance, sabotage and terrorism," Frank said.

Fearing a diplomatic incident, the CIA and other US agents rarely venture into Afghanistan. As a rule, soldiers from the British elite Special Air Service (SAS) work with and train the mujahedeen instead. SAS provided weapons training in Afghanistan until 1982 when Russian soldiers found the passports of two British instructors in a training camp. After that, the mujahedeen were trained in secret camps in remote parts of Scotland. [24]

Ken Connor, who served 23 years in the SAS, before starting a 'soldier for hire' Security Company, described the role of Special Forces as "providing military training" to the mujahedeen in Scotland.

The mujahedeen and Al-Qaeda's most infamous Saudi leader, the CIA and MI6 agent Osama Bin Laden benefited from British training. His bearded face with searing brown eyes glared out from TV screens in the homes of the Wests gullible public. Bin Laden became the devil incarnate, without reference to those who sat in London and Washington and Riyadh running the show.[25]

---

[24] http://www.historycommons.org/context.jsp?item=a1980mujaretrained

[25] Like Pablo Escobar the Mexican drug lord, he ended up being hunted and was assassinated before telling his story.
http://www.independent.co.uk/news/world/americas/robert-oneill-shot-dead-osama-bin-laden-abbottabad-pakistan-raid-2011-the-operator-book-a7710101.html

"I met some mujahedeen in India and Pakistan," I said, "they're the world's biggest Heroin Traffickers, heroin for arms was their sales gambit, 'they' want Afghanistan because it's just one big poppy field."

"Aye," Frank said.

"It's Vietnam all over again."

A flight attendant took her place in front of the aisle, her white face framed by red hair caught back in a serious bun. She completed her pre-flight safety demonstration watched by the disinterested passengers.

"Then there's the subs and the nukes; they were testing stonefish up at Lochalsh," Frank said.

Buckling up the seat belt, "Yes and SBS personnel at the 'Underwater Test and Evaluation Centre' also based at Kyle of Lochalsh were testing weapons. For that matter, Oban, where Kock lives, is just 68 miles from Invergarry."

"Aye, he does."

Scotland like Wales was awash with spies in the midst of the cold war taking their places on the chessboard. The black and white squares acting like the black and white castles in my identification training. You have to know which castle is dark and which is light I was told. The art of war is 'knowing,' not thinking, not working it out, not assessing, not investigating. *Had Willie been taught to distinguish the white castles from the black castles.*

"Willie was an insider working for Military Intelligence; did he ever work for six?"

"Six is ours, we 'ave to remember the're our service," he said, buckling his belt.

The flight attendant came down the aisle, her hard white legs contrasted against her tight fitting blue skirt. She glanced at our laps to check our belts, a tiny strand of her red-gold hair escaping from her coiffure. I smiled.

"Did 'Six' have a hand in the death of Willie MacRae?"

"I di na say that," he said, "he was a player, 'aye he was a player."

The visage of Willie shot before my eyes, rugged and warm; he was loved by and always there for his friends. They said Willie could never say no to someone in trouble.

Having graduated with a first in History from Glasgow University, Willie entered WW11 as an officer in the Seaforth Highlanders regiment. He fought in Europe then was posted under 'tricky Dickie' (Lord Mountbatten) to South East Asia. Mountbatten was later embroiled as a figurehead in General Kitson's Coup, a plot for a military coup to unseat Prime Minister Harold Wilson. This very British coup failed because officers who had come up through the ranks would not support it. More infamously, Mountbatten was to become involved in the Kincora Scandal in Northern Ireland, where boys in care were raped, sold, trafficked and used by MI5 as blackmail tools. Willie would not have taken advantage of children or used them expediently.

"Willie served under, Tricky Dickie and we all know his involvement with kids."

Frank leaned out to look up the aisle.

"It's no mi area."

"It never is, you can investigate arms, drugs, terrorism, but the moment you look at the child trafficking every door gets slammed in your face. If you're lucky you get to walk away."

His face composed itself into a mask.

"As I told you, it's no mi area."

"I heard Willie was friends with Indira Gandhi and also Ben-Gurion. He helped Israel draft their laws and when he died in his memory, they planted 3000 trees."

"He wus no a nobody," Frank said.

Willie MacRae was dead the moment he left Glasgow followed by two SB cars. A thorn in the side of the establishment amongst other things he campaigned against the dumping of nuclear waste in Scotland. Willie also helped the victims of state protected drugs traffickers. However, none of these annoyances to the State spelled his death sentence. As a lovable, charismatic firebrand Scottish Nationalist with a role in India's independence, Thatcher's Government loathed him. However, he was not murdered for his political activities.

The plane began to taxi. I looked out at nondescript buildings under a dark gray sky. I was happy to leave Glasgow behind as we soared into the heavens above the thick cloud layers.

The September before Willie's suiciding, Barbara Castle MP had her 'Pedophile files' openly seized by SB from Journalist Don Hale. One year before that Geoffrey Dickens MP in all innocence handed a similar file now known as the 'Dickens Dossiers' to the then Home Secretary Leon Brittan, which disappeared.[26]

While working with Tony Blair MP, then shadow Home Secretary, uncovering VIP pedophiles and police corruption, I arranged to meet Geoffrey Dickens. Geoff was a friend and fellow campaigner for children. In the green-carpeted hallways of Parliament, Geoff surreptitiously handed me parts of his ignored Dossiers. "You may be able to do something with these," he had told me looking over his shoulder at an imaginary enemy. Geoffrey Dickens, not unlike Willie MacRae was a larger than life character, honest, outspoken and passionate. Cramming the documents into my bag, I thanked him not knowing they contained evidence of and the names of VIP pedophiles.

Just before his death, Willie MacRae had likewise come into possession of and intended to expose, a similar dossier of evidence naming pedophile Politicians, Police, Judges and Civil Servants on both sides of the border.

Barbara Castle MP had complained that Home Secretary Leon Britten used SB as his own personal 'Gestapo'. On his last fateful journey from Glasgow to Dornie, Special Branch shadowed Willie. *Was Leon Brittan MP QC named in Willies dossier as it was in mine?*

As the plane soared into the air, causing my stomach to churn with the rush, the passengers continued their conversations.

"I wonder if Willie had similar evidence against the pedo's as

---

[26] Rolling onto 2014, Fiona Wolf then head of the ongoing UK Child abuse inquiry was forced to resign because of her personal relationship with Leon Britten, who was due to appear before the Inquiry to explain the disappearance of Geoffrey Dickens dossiers. He died before his appearance.

Geoff Dickens gave to me last November, Geoff seems to have been blocked at every stage; he's been burgled, threatened and put on a hit list," I said.

Frank bit his lip as if he was not keen on taking off.

Unlike Geoffrey Dickens, Barbara Castle and Don Hale, Willie could not be 'managed' by intimidation he had waited a long time to get evidence on 'them.' One of the last people to see Willie alive, former Strathclyde police officer Donald Morrison, said he saw two SB cars follow Willie as he drove out of Glasgow. I wonder he said,

"Knowing what we do know of the sex abuse and the names of some of the perpetrators is it probable Willie MacRae had come across some explosive evidence which is why he had to be silenced."

The dossier secreted in his briefcase, which never left his side, went with him to his death. Like Dickens and Castle's dossiers and the documents given to me by Dickens, they have been stolen and disappeared by the State.

"It's dangerous investigating pedophiles," I said, looking at the long drop to the world below me from the aircraft window.

SB has not given me the benefit of their report into the murder of their target, but watchers, watching them, informed me it was a bungled operation, covered-up by the Northern Constabulary.

Willies Holiday home in Dornie had been broken into before and searched. He told a friend they 'did not find what they were looking for.' Had Special Branch or MI5 stolen Willies antique revolver in one of their many burglaries in his homes. Then there is the mystery of what happened to Willie during the hours he was alone. What happened between the times he left Glasgow to when he was found next day in his rolled Volvo by an Australian tourist.

John Conway a former CID policeman who independently investigated the MacRae case said, MI5 was involved in the death and cover-up. In his final report submitted to the Lord Advocate, he stated on page 213:

"There can be no doubt that sometime after the crash and the first people arriving on the scene, someone searched through MacRae's pockets and also ransacked the car."

Mr. Conway himself suffered a serious accident, which he said was a 'frightener' gone wrong.[27]

"Aye, it's way too dangerous," Frank said, "ye should nay go there, or you'll end up dead like the others."

"I know, since getting Dickens documents my tires have been let down, wheel nuts undone and cherry on the cake they murdered the next door neighbor and then tried to set me. SB saved me from the Police."

"Saved you did they?" he said, with a wave of his hand. "Stick to arms, it's no so dangerous."

The firebrand Willie MacRae carried is still burning in the hearts of the Scottish people. Those who followed Willie believed his outstanding oratory and fearless integrity would lead Scotland to Independence.[28]

"Why is it so dangerous to investigate child abuse, Frank?"

Turning his head away from me, "It's no me area. It's all in the history," he said closing his eyes.

Once we arrived in Heathrow, we both looked for the exit. It was then I discovered that like me Frank had no sense of direction. Frank was relying on me and I was relying on him, it was doomed. Following a group of people who were surely on their way out, we ended up at the top of a flight of steps.

A fresh thirtysomething 'gray suit' shadow said, close to my ear, "If you go down there you will end up in Germany."

We both looked at him; Frank scowled in annoyance, looking daggers at me as if I was responsible for his embarrassment.

"East or West?" I jibed, at the clean-shaven watchers face. "Well. Which is the exit?"

---

[27] http://www.fantompowa.net/Flame/william_mcrae.htm

[28] Would the 2015 referendum for Scottish Independence have resulted in a 'Yes' vote had Willie MacRae not been suicided by the State?

Douglas Hoyle was waiting to meet Frank in Parliament, a safe enough place for them to meet although not secure.

The 'Arms to Iraq' crew was a small complement of intelligence agents, journalists, arms company insiders and MP's who delved into the whys and wherefores. It was the game of the century, each piece of the jigsaw was fought over, and by some, jealously guarded. Doug Hoyle MP is a man of discerning intelligence, a detective by nature with a thirst to get to the bottom of a problem. If anyone could corral Frank, Douglas could. And so, I left them alone together.

Paragraph 146 (now paragraph 156), read, amended and agreed to.

Paragraph 147 (now paragraph 157), read, amended and agreed to.

New paragraph--(*Mr Doug Hoyle*.)--brought up and read as follows:

"It seems hardly credible that a large military project such as Babylon would not have been known to British and other intelligence services. Dr Cowley claimed that at a very early stage he had personally kept the British intelligence service informed about this matter and to his knowledge Dr Bull had been in touch with the US and other intelligence services from the outset. Certainly Gumbley and James of Astra and Kock claimed they approached MoD and security services in September and October 1989, yet no statement was made to the House until April 1990. It is a serious matter that Ministers were not informed that brings into question accountability of intelligence sources to their responsible Ministers and we leave it to others to decide whether these matters should be considered elsewhere".

Question put, That the paragraph be added to the Report.

The Committee divided.

Ayes, 5	Noes, 5
Mr Menzies Campbell	Mr James Cran
Mr Jim Cousins	Sir Anthony Grant
Mr Stan Crowther	Dr Keith Hampson
Dr John Gilbert	Sir Robin Maxwell-Hyslop
Mr Doug Hoyle	Mr Barry Porter

Whereupon the Chairman declared himself with the Noes.

Question put, That the Report be the Second Report of the Committee to the House.

The Committee divided.

Ayes, 6	Noes, 4
Mr Menzies Campbell	Mr James Cran
Mr Jim Cousins	Sir Anthony Grant
Mr Stan Crowther	Dr Keith Hampson
Dr John Gilbert	Mr Barry Porter
Mr Doug Hoyle	
Sir Robin Maxwell-Hyslop	

Ordered, That the Chairman to make the Report to the House.

Motion made, and Question put, That certain papers relating to Sheffield Forgemasters be appended to the Minutes of Evidence.--(*Dr Keith Hampson.*)

The Committee divided.

Ayes, 1	Noes, 6
Dr Keith Hampson	Mr Menzies Campbell
	Mr Jim Cousins
	Mr Stan Crowther
	Dr John Gilbert
	Mr Doug Hoyle
	Sir Robin Maxwell-Hyslop

Ordered, That the Appendices to the Minutes of Evidence taken before the Committee be reported to the House.

Resolved, That the Committee record their appreciation of the services of Mr Kenneth Warren as Chairman of the Committee since 1983.--(*Sir Robin Maxwell-Hyslop.*)

Not included in the Select Committee Report

14. A NADIR

Pushing another twenty round magazine into the AR15, I aimed and fired. With a muzzle-brake on the end, it barely moved. The bullets flew onto the target, blat blat blat as I emptied the magazine. Light and accurate, it outranked standard issue by miles.

Lowering the rifle, I turned to flame-haired Robert standing to my left. Since our last meeting overlooking Bardsey Island he had developed a presidential presence, but still smiled like a lothario.

"It's a great weapon, finely balanced," I said.

Removing the spent magazine, I handed the AR15 back to Robert. A burnt powder and metal smell coming up from the muzzle mingled with his aftershave.

Bagging the AR, he took out a long gun case and placed it on the side-table, clicking open the catches.

"Take a look at this."

The silver streak in his auburn hair drew my gaze; I noticed a fresh sprinkling of gray at the temples. While his nondescript suit, in the finest materials clung to his body, as a rag clings to a flagpole.

"What is it?"

"Sauer M30 combination issued by the Luftwaffe."

The gun nestling in the oak and leather case looked like a shotgun until I spotted the third rifled barrel inside.

"Where did you get it?"

Taking it lovingly out of the box, "It was my fathers," he said.

"So why are you here, it's not just to see me is it?"

"Oh, you know I have just brought Machon down with me to see Doug Hoyle."

"How did it go?"

"Frank's still like a Mustang being corralled. I left him with Dougy, who is a practiced diplomat."

"Let's see."

"Gerald James says Kock took out Bull and Johnathan Moyal."

Sitting down on a nearby stool, he said, "They have a manual you know. Few agents realize that the moment they step through the welcoming door of the murky intelligence world their death or imprisonment is meticulously planned on an, if need, basis."

The soft hazel depth of his eyes with the green flecks drew me in as I looked up.

"All services?"

He nodded in reply.

That explained why similar techniques are used to eliminate targets by intelligence agencies all over the world. Women's clothing, child abuse images, bondage equipment, these are common themes in the deaths of British officials and agents. We began walking again.

"But why make it so awful? Johnathan Moyal hanging in a wardrobe with a pillowcase thrust over his head."

"The operational manual includes setting the scene to appear like a perverted sexual fantasy which overreached itself."

"But why?"

"Family and friends are bewildered and embarrassed, so fail to question the official version. Then it slips from public memory."

He put the lid back on his bullet case, "It also acts as a media field trial. Very obviously, murder an important target, say it was suicide, plant stories with media friendlies, and corral the public to turn on the victim. Result zero sympathy for the victim's horrific death. Job done."

"What about me?"

"Oh, it doesn't work so well with the ladies."

A twinkle in his eye hit me like a shooting star.

"You were on a target list, now you are on a protected list."

"A target list?"

He nodded, "Those considered dangerous go on the target list, those involved in activism go on the activists' list. The protected go on the protected list. Did you ever wonder why you can break all the speed limits in North Wales?"

"I sort of understood it, but it's difficult putting it all together when life is such a roller coaster."

"There are local lists and National lists, you're not protected yet, so watch your back."

"How does it work?"

"Get on the protected list and you won't be prosecuted for anything. If you were caught breaking some law, a call would be made, and any evidence would disappear,"

"Disappear! No matter what you had done,"

"Oh, it doesn't matter, rape, murder, terrorism, theft, fraud. The evidence would disappear."

"And if you're on a target list?" I said, grabbing a stool to sit opposite him.

"In that case, the slightest misdemeanor brings prosecution and harassment. If a target has a vehicle, they will be stopped everywhere for spurious reasons," he leaned towards me. "But for those considered really dangerous, another rule comes into play. They used to plant drugs, but it's getting more sophisticated, new will laws mean targets can be set-up for almost anything. Fishing through a targets record, they can unearth something forgotten from ten, twenty, thirty years ago and resurrect. The target finds it difficult to believe the same State which encouraged them to break the rules will use any devious, corrupt means to break them because of it."

"All this is so costly. It's hard enough getting your mileage allowance from them."

"It's not their money. It's the taxpayers, they have bottomless pockets to go after perceived enemies, the whole system supports ridding the State of dangerous people who might disrupt or expose ongoing operations."

Shaking my head, "And the agents who are programmed?"

"No-one knows what's hidden in their subconscious, ready to leap out. The difference with those who are programmed is that hidden elements are placed there for a purpose."

I shuddered. *What lurked inside my subconscious?* Something he had said caused the steady rhythm of my lifeblood to stop.

Ignoring the dour look, he said, "The murder of insider's acts as a silencer to those who may consider talking and as black entertainment to those who watch their plan unfurl."

"What about Kock, he seems a bit flamboyant, the opposite of secret."

"Oh, their arrogance knows no bounds. Kock's in with Thatcher; he's their bagman,[29] knows where all the backhanders and money flow from covert deals goes. He was brought in from MITS.[30]

---

[29] CIA report stamped November 1991 explained Kock was responsible for the murder of Bull and Moyal then led inevitably to the dirty profits made from illegal arms sales. The intelligence specialist explained Margaret Thatcher's son Mark had "received £12 million from a weapons sale and Nadir's company Polly Peck tried to cover it." http://www.independent.co.uk/voices/comment/the-supergun-plot-murders-and-a-report-we-cant-ignore-9382688.html

[30] MITS ((secret part of Midland Bank) later rebranded HSBC. July 2016 the Guardian wrote that, 'The US government decided not to pursue criminal charges against HSBC for allowing terrorists and drug dealers to launder millions of dollars after George Osborne and the UK banking regulator intervened to warn that prosecuting Britain's biggest bank could lead to a global financial disaster".

"Midland, the Royal Bank of Scotland run via Younger, Nat West all money-laundering fronts for the Club. It's the bankers." He said, leaning against the wooden table.

"Younger, he is also involved in running Allivane."

"Yes, that's right."

"So the banks act like front companies. And these front companies run the economy of the world?" I asked.

"Not quite," he said smiling. "It's a debt slave system where even those not jailed by the system do not see the chains. Brought up to believe fictional Governments run Countries for their benefit and make laws to protect them. They believe bits of printed paper have value. It's a simple bluff that works over and over again. Creating Nations of debt slaves to fictional governments and fictional economies."

Robert glanced at me. His knowledge was seeping into me by osmosis, and a growing comprehension was taking shape.

"I understand. Then people actively take part in voting in one slave master after another, believing things will change, but, of course, they never do."

"That's right, they never do," he nodded.

"What about Switzerland how does it fit in?"

"Switzerland and Cyprus both places are awash with laundering banks, big banks, small banks. Russian banks full of ex KGB mafia money, like Alpha bank. Then there are the politician's kickbacks from arms deals, contract placements, child porn, drugs, people trafficking, with the Bank of International Settlements holding a special place." [31]

---

https://www.theguardian.com/business/2016/jul/11/hsbc-us-money-laundering-george-osborne-report

[31] In 2007, Hudes a Senior Counsel in the World Bank was fired for blowing the whistle on banking corruption. She exposed the global financial system was dominated by a small corrupt group centering around the US Federal Reserve. This group created debt slaves of the world's free peoples "with something known as state capture, which is where the institutions of government are co-opted by the group that's corrupt." Karen said a network including 147 institutions and central banks controlled 40 per cent of the total wealth of a   network of 43,000 Multi-

"Cyprus is interesting, with its connections with Serbia and the arms being funneled through Yugoslavia to Iraq, Belgrade and Bulls Blaise Bleed 155's," I said.

"There's a network running through Cyprus, receiving billions from Serbia and funneling it out to the accounts of numerous offshore companies in Panama, Lichtenstein Nassau, and Switzerland."

"So, on the outside companies like Asil Nadirs Unipac fit neatly into this system," I said.[32]

"Machon was involved with Unipac delivering Propellant for the big gun."

"Yes, I know I asked him about it, but he just wittered on about a chocolate egg," I said.

"Well, it was disguised as chocolate." [33]

National Corporations., creating a "super-entity." Barclays Bank, JPMorgan Chase & Co, Deutsche Bank AG and The Goldman Sachs Group were named in the top 20 group from where the U.S. Federal Reserve "secretly dominated the world economy." In addition, the Swiss Bank for International Settlements acting as "the club of these central banks." http://www.kahudes.net/wp-content/uploads/2012/05/ilsaJournal1.pdf

[32] Tycoon and Tory Party Donner Asil Nadir certainly was expendable, a couple of months later he was charged with fraud. Northern Ireland Minister Michael Mates rushed to Nadir's defense but was then forced to resign. Nadir fled to Cyprus knowing he would not receive a fair trial in a system designed to cover-up the cabal's criminal empire. In 2010, following promises from the Prosecution Nadir returned voluntarily to the United Kingdom hoping to clear his name and move on. He flew into London just ten days after Gareth Williams body was discovered in the sports –bag, 2010, the year that the Conservative party won the election under David Cameron, was a year for tying up loose ends.

[33] November 1991 CIA page 24 said about my erstwhile buddy Frank Machon 'As the UN initiated a ceasefire in the Iran-Iraq War, and the UK relaxed arms to Iraq guidelines, Allivane and the Ministry of Defense (MoD) used new covert routes to conceal irregular arms consignments. Frank Machon based in Scotland, had shipped huge consignments of fuses produced by Royal Ordnance, and subsequently, the trucking agent shipped smaller consignments of fuses disguised as automobile components and a test consignment of Bull's supergun propellant disguised as chocolate destined for packaging by Unipac based in Cyprus, before shipment to Jordan. Subsequently, the Royal Air Force shipped similar covert consignments to Jordan via Cyprus. (S NF NC)'

"That's probably why. And what about Kock?" I asked.

"It's a tight circle; Kock is a trusted servant and keeper of many dark secrets,"

"So Did Kock murder, Jonathan Moyle?"

"Moyle knew both of his killers. You should ask Machon." [34] he replied.

A clicking noise outside made us both turn our heads towards the door, but it was just electric running through a fuse box.

"Illegal shipments are delivered, evidence collected, then when new routes are opened with arms running to different countries, they take down the edifice they built. Removing fall guys, people and companies who have outlived their usefulness. On the periphery, companies peopled by the expendable are set-up to fall. You know how it works," he said.

"Yes, I know, you're a dead duck if you expose on-going routes or where the kickbacks are stashed," I agreed.

"There's a lot of expendable front people in the chain. Whenever a company is formed, or a group of people assembled there are those who are expendable - useful for the duration of the enterprise but eliminated once their usefulness has ended. Taken out, jailed, disappeared, suicided, neutralized. Look at Matrix."

Earlier that year in March, Customs Investigations teams A and B based in London commenced an investigation of Matrix Churchill's machine tool exports to Iraq. In April Customs had just arrested Peter Mitchell, Managing Director of Walter Somers plus a scientist and charged them in connection with "Supergun." [35]

---

[34]   CIA report November 1991 led straight as an arrow to the bulls-eye back to Kock, Bull, Moyal and 'Arms to Iraq' The report confirms "Kock hired two ex-SAS assassins Jon Jack and Terry Harding to eliminate Bull." Kock also found that defense journalist, Jonathan Moyle, was in possession of evidence of UK covert arms deals. So Koch and Holdness (MI6) eliminated him in Santiago, Chile.'

[35]   April 11th, 1990 'Customs seize Supergun'
http://news.bbc.co.uk/onthisday/hi/dates/stories/april/11/newsid_2477000/24 77023.stm

David James, Chairman of Eagle Trust the ultimate owners of Walter Somers, said he had been working with MI6 to find 'Supergun.' David James's story might have been more convincing if a model of Supergun had not been displayed at the Bagdad Arms Fair in 1989 where MI6 were present along with other British representatives.

Dereck Duberry was one of the Customs Officers investigation 'arms to Iraq'. Dereck was a young man with the contained eagerness of an adolescent greyhound. Dereck's team were aware Matrix Churchill's directors Paul Henderson, Abraham and Allen were fall guys. Paul Henderson was also an MI6 informant. I made it crystal clear to Customs during meetings that the Conservative Government were behind all the illegal sales of arms to Iraq and that Alan Clark, Minister for Defence Procurement, was lying in the interview he gave to them. Dereck knew Clark was lying but said:

"How can you tell a Minister he's lying?"[36]

The prosecution of the innocent Matrix directors went ahead regardless.

"I had a meeting with Dereck Duberry as no doubt you know?" Robert nodded. "They know Clarke is lying, but the prosecution is going ahead." [37]

---

[36] In November Alan Clark admitted he had been 'economical with the truth' Customs withdrew all charges against Walter Somers people without explanation. The prosecution against Matrix Churchill spectacularly collapsed.
http://www.independent.co.uk/news/clark-scandal-descends-into-tales-of-blackmail-and-lechery-[19683.html
https://www.theguardian.com/world/defence-and-security-blog/2012/nov/09/arms-iraq-saddam-hussein

[37] If the prosecution of the Matrix directors been withdrawn then the 'Scott Inquiry' into Arms to Iraq would not have taken place. In November 1992 Lord Justice Scott's inquiry into 'arms to Iraq' was announced. The cat was indeed out of the bag and the illegal arms trade was talked about everywhere. Government corruption and deception, the betrayal of armed service personnel, had captured the minds of the public, allowing them to peek behind the curtain of a secret world where power politics and secret deals took place.
http://www.independent.co.uk/news/uk/matrix-churchill-case-was-ludicrous-former-minister-could-not-see-justification-for-trial-david-1467481.html

Hansard Matrix Churchill HC Deb 10 November 1992 vol 213 cc743-58

"Clarke is also expendable, Even those who inhabit the top rungs can find the position they have grasped difficult to hold and dangerous to have," he said.

Once I had the misfortune to meet Alan Clarke MP he was an arrogant womanizer and pedophile. His dirty secrets were covered up by Max Clifford, [38] another arrogant womanizer, and convicted pedophile. Clifford was the best friend of my amigo, lap dance king, Steve Less, while Steve despite his sordid business did not interfere with the Girls; Clifford was another kettle of fish. Alan Clarke had the conscience of a Piccadilly madam, and his sole redeeming feature was that, like me, he was a vegetarian.

"It's more than money, of course, they, print money. They own the banks and the multinationals. It is all expendable, except the System," he concluded.

"Say hi to the big man," I said. "Oh and have a safe journey."

"I am flying out of Greenham."

We walked together to the exit.

Robert's bulk framed in the doorway by the dying light, a buffalo with the spirit of an eagle. We parted with a nod.

---

[38] Max Clifford talks about Alan Clarke on video
https://www.youtube.com/watch?v=u8m4sSCEZlU

15. SUFFER LITTLE CHILDREN

"Children were denied a childhood, an identity, a family and any sense of belonging. Many, some as young as three, were sent abroad, often having been falsely told their parents were dead. The sheer scale of sexual abuse of British-born girls and boys could be worse than in the Savile scandal and further children's homes outrages we are aware of." Gordon Brown former UK Prime Minister

The young man with the finely chiseled features sat wringing his hands as tears like poor quality diamonds, rolled down his cheeks and fragmented into his lap. We sat on stark wooden chairs in his girlfriend's kitchen as he shared his pain.

One moment before I had sat with a charming, strong and good-looking twenty-something man. Then, as he talked about the abuse he suffered as a child, he transformed in front of me into a frightened little boy.

As Joel sat there crying, I wanted to hug him, wipe away his tears and tell him it would be all right but I could not. It would not be all right; I could not make it right, no one had been there for him when he was a terrified little boy.

A beautiful blond Celtic child, he had been at Bryn Alyn Children's home taken there at the age of ten. I had met his mother and sisters. They were sturdy and proud, and would have made excellent Celtic warrior women in ages past. Joel was torn from his family, perhaps because of his beauty, which was prized by pedophiles. The family peace was shattered, by the rape, abuse and subsequent persecution of their son and brother. No one spoke of the father, and I did not ask.

"When you can. Tell me where you were abused?"

"I was taken from Bryn Alyn to a big house near Chester," he said, "it had portraits on the walls."

"Would you remember it if you saw it again?"

"Yes, I remember, I cannot forget, I want to, but I cannot forget."

A shock of dirty blond hair fell over his clean-shaven face, the bright white skin of his strong arms bulged beneath his short-sleeved T-shirt. If you met him on the street, you would not imagine the grief carried secretly within

"They sent me for Electric Shock Treatment at the hospital to make me forget."

"At what age?"

"I was ten," he whimpered his face screwed up. "But I did not forget I just pretended to forget."

Many of these children whose youth is an object of sexual desire become lost in the child abuse image trade, where they are further abused, tortured and even murdered on camera. Others die from drugs or neglect, the life expectancy of children in this business is short. Joel had survived because of his close family ties.

"Who abused you in the big house?" I asked.

"They sold me to an old man he was a Lord or something."

"Could you describe him?"

"Yes, I remember every detail, I remember his smell."

"When you have time, will you write it all down for me so we can identify this man?"

"Yes, I will," he said, trembling. "I ran away many times the first time I went to the Police and told them about the abuse and being sold."

"What happened?"

"They laughed at me," he said, as more tears escaped from his tormented heart.

"They took me back and I was beaten and thrown into solitary. I ran away twice more, but every time the Police took me back and the beatings got worse."

Bringing back memories had devastated him, so I did not want to press him further.

"We can talk another day," I said, rising to go.

State child abuse opens a curtain into a hidden and frightening part of our psyche: the first time we became self-aware, separate and alone, the first time we experience unadulterated pain and fear. Children torn from their own quiet awakening into a world where these horrors become a living part of their lives are forever struggling not to drown in their own sorrow.

I had felt the barb of fear as a child and empathized with Joel's struggle to come to some terms with his childhood terrors. Joel was at the blunt end of British State organized child trafficking, which was a long-standing policy of a debauched political class.

Politicians made laws allowing children to be seized from their parents and sold into sex slavery while Police and Judges enforce these laws acting as enablers.

Between 1920 and 1974, one hundred and thirty thousand British children torn from their families and homeland were transported to Australia, Canada, New Zealand and Southern Rhodesia (now Zimbabwe).[39] Vulnerable children ended up as sex slaves, all with the stamp of the law.

---

[39] Gordon Brown MP apologizes to trafficked children calling the transportation a "modern form of government- induced trafficking".
https://www.theguardian.com/uk-news/2017/jul/20/forced-migration-britain-uk-worst-child-abuse-scandal-gordon-brown-inquiry

Meanwhile, other children languished in British Children's Homes where they were sexually, physically and psychologically abused and often prostituted.[40] Still worse, the Courts sent children to Approved Schools, Borstals, Remand Homes and Correction Centers where many were tortured, raped and beaten. Magistrates and Judges who condemn these children use trite legal phrases and excuses like Care and Protection Orders,[41] dooming children to a lifetime of suffering.

With Police protecting child traffickers and conversely threatening the trafficked children if they complained. With a justice system designed to punish abused children and keep a constant supply chain for child traffickers like Sir Jimmy Savile, the Krays twins and those less well-known criminals running Children's Homes. With traffickers and their customers dining with Police chiefs, Judges, Royals and Members of Parliament, the children had no-where to turn for help.

However, not all of Britain's elite profited directly or by their silence from child trafficking, some raised their heads above the parapet and fought against the system. Geoffrey Dickens MP was one of these brave fighters. He had campaigned to help abused children since 1981, when he named MI6 agent and former British High Commissioner to Canada, Sir Peter Hayman, as a pedophile in the House of Commons.

Victims, child protection officers, worried parents and campaigners flocked to Geoffrey to give him information and evidence of child trafficking; this included the names of senior men in his own Conservative Party. From the evidence emerged a VIP pedophile ring networking between Parliament, Buckingham Palace, the Civil Service, including Intelligence chiefs and other areas soaking up public money.

---

[40] Lambeth Council pay tens of millions of pounds to survivors of child abuse. https://www.theguardian.com/society/2016/dec/15/lambeth-council-pay-tens-of-millions-pounds-child-abuse-survivors-shirley-oaks and https://www.lambeth.gov.uk/SOSA

[41] Personal Social Services: Reviews of United Kingdom Statistical Sources.By B. P. Davies Page 9 Butterworth-Heinemann, 2014 ISBN 1483193144, 9781483193144

Compiling the evidence into dossiers in 1984, Geoffrey handed them over to the then Home Secretary Leon Brittan QC who promised to do something. Geoffrey told me that after this he was "burgled, followed and harassed." The name Leon Brittan OC was later added to his dossiers as a pedophile.

Geoffrey was a larger than life character a former boxer an eccentric and a most admirable man; it was his campaign to help children, which had drawn me to him. The investigation led to a Pan-European network linked to what would become known as Operation Gladio. The network running alongside NATO's official Intelligence service also ran terrorist groups. We had laughed about checking under our cars for bombs and wept together for the children we could not save.

Dennis Parry was the Labour leader of Clwyd Council and another campaigner for abused children. On my way to London, I stopped off to meet him.

Dennis stood up as I approached him and held out his soft thinker's hand, which I clasped. We were meeting, for the first time, for a quick coffee in a small country restaurant near Colwyn Bay. A pot of coffee and two cups already graced the simple table with the blue and white chinze tablecloth.

Dennis had a reputation for integrity and for exposing corruption. He worked with a small group of people in powerful local positions who were aware of Police corruption, child trafficking and a child abuse image empire presided over by North Wales Police. In this group were Dennis, Harry Templeton a brave and resolute North Wales Police whistleblower, Malcomb King Social Services chief and John Marek Labour Member of Parliament for Wrexham.

Dennis fitted in some jigsaw pieces of the child abuse network, puzzle. He told me about the arrest by Railway Police of Sir Peter Morrison, the MP for Chester and Margaret Thatcher's Personal Private Secretary. Morrison was detained for sexually abusing a young boy on a train until instruction 'arrived from above' and the Railway Police were forced to let the pedophile Sir Peter Morrison go.

"The Railway Police are still angry about being forced to let Morrison go; then there's Chief Superintended Gordon Anglesea and his Masonic lodge brimming with North Wales Police Officers," he said.

"Yes, Anglesea is a major player in North Wales along with another nineteen named police officers, all Masons. I have been talking with Geoffrey Dickens about Gladio and the role of the Masons in child abuse. There is a lot to learn about how it all fits together. How does Chief Constable David Owen, slot into this?"

"He covers up for them," Dennis said. "We have to get a Public Inquiry to expose the whole lot of them." Dennis said.

"Yes, that is what everyone is campaigning for."

Together with Politicians, the Press and concerned others, I campaigned to have an all-reaching Public Inquiry set-up. We wanted an Inquiry to investigate the sexual, physical and psychological abuse of children from Care Homes.

Victims claimed to have been abused by the Directors and staff of the Children's Homes and members of the extended pedophile network, which included famous names, police officers, politicians, businessmen and members of the legal profession including judges.

Whistle-blowers and victims, without which the truth would never be told, were being targeted to silence them. We called for an investigation into the on-going cover-up.

"We are also looking for a Labour win in the next election to change things."

"Labour will win when Kinnock exposes the Government is illegally selling arms to Iraq, We supplied him will the evidence."

"But Kinnock supported war with Iraq," Dennis said.

The month before in August 1990, Neil Kinnock had supported the UK and USA in a call for war with Iraq. Despite the fact he knew both Governments were illegally selling arms to Iraq and that British and American service personnel would face the weapons their own governments had covertly sold. At that time, Johnny (John Smith MP) was shadow Chancellor of the Exchequer in Kinnock's Cabinet. Johnny, who knew about the illegal sales of arms to Iraq refused to take part in the debate where Neil Kinnock had convinced the Labour shadow Cabinet to support war with Iraq.

"Yes, he did support war with Iraq, and that is very worrying."

"Apart from Kinnock, who are you dealing with?" Dennis asked.

"Gerald Kaufman, he wants to spill the beans, John Smith he opposes Kinnock's stance on Iraq. Then there's Allan Rogers, Doug Hoyle, and Robin Cook, but it is up to Kinnock. Expect he is waiting to drop it like a bomb during the run-up to the election. When the date is announced," I said, standing up. "Dennis it's really good to meet you."

"Yes, we must meet again soon," He said walking with me to restaurant door. "Have a good journey. I will ring you," Dennis said as we parted.

During the run-up to the April 1992 General election, I waited for Kinnock to expose the 'arms to Iraq' scandal and tell the British Public about the covert and illegal arms deals the Tories made with Iraq.

As the days ticked by it dawned on me, Kinnock was not going to say anything or allow Gerald Kaufman to say anything. Therefore, Neil Kinnock MP handed victory to the Tories and then resigned as leader of the Labour Party. His payoff was high position in Europe and a Knighthood.[42]

Johnny Smith QC became Labour Party leader. Scottish Johnny was a remarkable politician who seemed to care. He knew about the Westminster Pedophile ring and the child abuse cover-up.[43] Now that

---

[42] Kinnock was appointed to the European Commission as Transport Commissioner in 1995. Later becoming a Vice-President of the European Commission. In 2005 he was made a life peer of the House of Lords.

[43] Smith was named as Parliamentarian of the year twice; the first time in November 1986 for his performances during the Westland Controversy where pedophile Leon Britten was forced to resign. Six months later he collapsed being examined at Edinburgh Royal Infirmary. He was told "**Whatever it is, we don't think it is your heart**" but in 1994 he died unexpectedly of a heart attack aged 55yrs. Insiders feared he had made a powerful enemy in Leon Brittan by threatening to expose him.

he was in a position to do something, he instructed rising star Tony Blair, whom he had made Home Secretary in his Shadow Government to liaise with me.

Tony Blair was ambitious and charming I found it easy to believe he meant to expose the complicity of Police and VIP's in organized child abuse.[44] We were working to an agenda I understood where the press, politicians, and activists worked together towards a common goal. Letters were excellent evidence and a simple means of keeping permanent records. Then, mysteriously the letters and notes to Tony Blair began to disappear, as did notes I sent to Simon Reagan.

The Labour idea was to confront Tory Home Secretary Kenneth Clarke QC about Police complicity in child trafficking and abuse.[45] So in August 1992, I wrote to Ken Clarke, after which Tony Blair wrote to Clarke about the content of my letter.

[44] Britain's top cop was an Assistant Chief Constable at Merseyside in 1998 when the force uncovered claims one of Tony Blair's ministers was a suspected pedophile http://www.mirror.co.uk/news/uk-news/metropolitan-police-chief-sir-bernard-5353419

[45] Ben Fellows a child actor accused Ken Clarke QC of groping him. The Police arrested Ben and the Crown prosecution service prosecuted him for perverting the course of justice. A jury found Ben not guilty. However former Home Secretary Kenneth Clarke QC has still not been arrested for perverting the course of justice. https://www.theguardian.com/politics/2015/jul/30/actor-kenneth-clarke-sexual-assault-perverting-course-of-justice

From: Tony Blair M.P.

HOUSE OF COMMONS
LONDON SW1A 0AA
Tel: 071- 219 4456
Constituency Tel: 0429- 882202

Ms. Tara Davison,
3 Gilfach Wen,
Penlon,
Menai Bridge,
Ynys Mon,
Gwynedd,
LL59 5QN.

12 November 1992

Dear Ms. Davison,

Thank you for your letter of 31 October, which I only received yesterday. It takes some time for post to find its way from our Head Office at Walworth Road to the House of Commons. As far as your letter of 30 September 1992 is concerned, I can assure you it did not arrive in my office here. My staff are usually meticulous about the mail and they assure me they have no record.

I enclose a letter I have written to the Home Secretary today; as soon as I receive a reply I will forward it to you. Alun Michael MP, Shadow Minister for Home Affairs and the member in my team responsible for crime is also apprised of the situation, and has been acting in conjunction with John Marek MP. As you are aware, local MPs have for some time been calling for an outside force to take over the investigation.

Yours sincerely,

Tony Blair MP.

Clarke and the Home Office refused to address the issue of child abuse or police corruption. Of course, this was not a surprise to anyone.

QUEEN ANNE'S GATE LONDON SW1H 9AT

11 DEC 1992

Our Ref: PCP/92 14/11/4 (S)
           PO 23087/92

Thank you for your letters of 4, 12 and 16 November, enclosing
correspondence from Ms Tara Andrea Davison of Ty Newyedd,
Rhyd-y-Groes, Pentir, Gwynedd, about the child abuse
investigations in North Wales.

Ms Davison has received a reply to her letter to me of
14 September, calling for the involvement of an outside police
force in the investigations. A copy of the reply is enclosed for
your information. You may find it helpful if I provide some
background details as neither Ms Davison's letter nor our reply
give full details of the alleged police involvement in this case.

A police investigation was conducted into allegations of child
abuse in North Wales in 1986 and the evidence was submitted to the
Crown Prosecution Service (CPS). On that occasion, the CPS decided
to take no further action.

The present investigation began in August 1991, following a number
of allegations about both physical and sexual abuse in children's
homes in Clwyd and Gwynedd. The allegations were directed mainly
against local authority employees in charge of the homes but also
suggested the involvement of a former Superintendent and Constable
of North Wales Police. Thirty police officers are engaged on the
investigation which is looking at allegations going back at least
12 years. The investigation is likely to last for some
considerable time but several people have already been charged with
offences.

Allegations, though not of _sexual_ abuse, have been made against
three serving police officers. At the first mention of serving
police officers being involved, Mr David Owen, the Chief Constable
reported the matter to the Police Complaints Authority (PCA). That
Authority maintained close liaison with the North Wales Police but
did not consider it necessary to intervene in the investigations.
All the investigations against serving police officers have been

\completed

Tony Blair Esq MP

completed and the reports sent to the Crown Prosecution Service who decided to take no further action. The PCA has also examined the reports and decided that no disciplinary action should be taken against two of the officers concerned. The remaining case is still being considered by the PCA.

Under section 86 of the Police and Criminal Evidence Act 1984, the investigation of allegations of misconduct by a Chief Officer of police is the responsibility of the relevant Police Authority. If Ms Davison has any evidence to substantiate her allegations that Mr Owen has conspired with others to cover up criminal activities, then she should approach the Police Authority with her evidence. I do have the power to order an Inquiry but I would only use it where there was serious doubt as to the policing of an area. Reports by Her Majesty's Inspector of Constabulary have shown that this is not the case in North Wales.

I cannot involve myself in the conduct of a police investigation nor can I direct a Chief Constable to involve another police force in an investigation. Such matters, as has already been explained to Ms Davison, are entirely the responsibility of the Chief Officer of the force concerned.

KENNETH CLARKE

Kenneth Clarke QC, however, did do something. Following his meeting with Leon Brittan, QC, Geoffrey Dickens had said,

"I was burgled, followed and harassed."

Throughout this period, I was, like Geoffrey Dickens, burgled, followed and harassed.[46]

---

[46] When John Smith MP died suddenly and unexpectedly I knew we were indeed as Barbara Castle put it "fighting a formidable foe"

16 . BIRTHDAY CARD

"I certainly think that another Holocaust can happen again. It did already occur; think of Cambodia, Rwanda, and Bosnia." Miep Gies

A tall gray-suited automaton pushed open the double doors with an elegant swish, ushering us into a corridor shaped foyer he abruptly retreated. I heard the slap-slap as the doors closed behind him.

Pete and I stood still, shocked by our sudden entry. Silence hung like a cloud, as the faces of two police officers standing behind a high desk slowly turned towards us in unison moving like choreographed dancers. Before the show began, the poignant pause was shattered as the doors opposite opened.

Peter Hain, Labour party MP for Neath, charged into the room as if escaping from an armed assassin. Disheveled, he gave the impression of a protester who had just put down his banner. Gray hair sprinkled his temples giving his urgent manner a small touch of eminence.

"Were you followed?" He said, conspiratorially.

Anxious, we both looked behind us as if to catch the fleeting glimpse of a spectral spy turning a corner that did not exist. Bringing my gaze back, my eyes engaged with the smiling faces of the two policemen. They noted every detail, the boredom of their day dissipated by the engaging pantomime.

"I don't think so," I said, re-establishing my nonchalance.

Peter Hain passed his gaze around the room, ignoring the

smirks of the Police. He beckoned us to follow him with such a damming air of secrecy. We dare not speak. The man whose back we followed as he climbed the stairs was destined to become Secretary of State for Northern Ireland and Minister for Europe.

Journalist Pete Sawyer and I were invited to a secret meeting with Peter Hain, along with nuclear expert and Guardian journalist David Lowry. On the table was the strange and troubling matter of a stolen British nuclear warhead.

The sticky fingers of the elite cabal who had armed and then destroyed Iraq was all over the disappearance.[47]

We trudged up the stairs following Peter Hain like lost sheep. Stepping into his parliamentary office, tables strewn with haphazard papers met the eye while boxes of documents lay deposited like stones in a dry riverbed. It was more a campaign headquarters than an office, *'Who could work here?'* I pondered straightening my flame brown silk skirt. Haines's index finger came to rest against his lips like the sudden landing of a large pink butterfly. Fascinated, we watched his finger as it behooved us to remain silent. Rolling his watery blue eyes around the plain walls, he aptly expressed that, these walls had ears. Calm and quiet as the office appeared, there lurked an inherent danger it was bugged. So we three, as if suspended in time, huddled together like star rugby players watched by a silent crowd waiting for play to begin.

Following the sound of a soft step outside in the corridor, a face appeared through the door, a jovial pleasant face like a fresh washed schoolboy.

---

[47] Later, using allied drugs lords, they would storm into Afghanistan using the might of US and UK Military to save the poppy harvest from rival Taliban and religious drug objectors. They named their military operation 'Enduring Freedom' laughing at the irony. The result saw Afghanistan transform into an opium plantation supplying 90% of the world's heroin. The cabal would arrange and back the Arab Spring creating enduring conflict in Egypt, Bahrain, Libya, Syria and Yemen. They would take down, thorn in their side, flamboyant Gadhafi, and force the wild Arab stallion to the ground, roped then haltered. They still run operations in Syria causing a mounting death toll. Pictures of disheveled children stare out of our newspapers asking us to 'care'. So much death, dismemberment and bloody destruction in the name of fighting terrorism and preserving world peace!

David Lowry walked into the room a few extra pounds graced him well, giving him an elegant bearing and a manner to match. There was something warm and wholesome about David that dispelled the furtive gloom and brought a ray of sunshine into the darkness of our pensive thoughts.

David's arrival precipitated further adventure into the rabbit hole as Peter glided passed him into the corridor, at the same time beckoning to us. No one spoke as the mime continued. One moment we were bustled into the corridor and then chaperoned into the next room where the door closed behind us with a dull thud. Peter and David, perfectly synchronized looked up at a seemingly innocent medium sized brown radio nestling on a high shelf. With a deft and practiced hand, Peter reached up to turn the small light brown Nob. Music and crackle erupted into the room like an invading army. The spell broken, we settled down to business, all heads together like conspirators plotting a revolution in an 18th century French inn.

"It's not safe to talk in my office," Peter said, just in case we had not the wits to notice the obvious. "So we're borrowing this one."

His manner was straightforward as if these shenanigans were natural in a Parliamentary building which of course they were.

"Do you have the documents?" Peter asked, referring to the statements, he had insisted we make.

Rumbling through my worn brown leather handbag, I brought out the crumpled sheets, while at the same moment Pete took his neat, crisp copies from his black briefcase. We placed them all crumpled and pristine into Peter's outstretched hand. With a flourish, he stood up opening a battleship gray safe in the wall. The door hung open for a moment, as he thrust our statements inside.

After an imperceptible pause, David turned to us with a serious expression.

"We have seen the photo's Green Peace took; showing the warhead being transported from Coulport to Burghfield, probably for reprocessing. Are you going to use them?" He said.

Coulport on the bank of Lock Fyfe in Strathclyde is a submarine base for Trident, and Burghfield is the Nuclear weapons manufacturing plant in Berkshire, just three miles from Aldermaston where the weapons are designed. The photos were taken by Green Peace ignoring the illegality of their shoot. They photographed the weapons as they moved in convoy along with their scoop pictures of the weapons stalwart uniformed guardians.

"Yes," Pete said confidently. "We are definitely going to publish."

Pete Sawyer was a quenched firebrand; somehow, the public school he had attended had squashed his free spirit while giving him a fine clipped tone accent. 30 years old with straight jet-black glossy hair that somehow always looked askew, he presented the unusual as normal. Dressing impeccably on a shoestring, he had discovered all the best London charity shops so found the top hand me downs. Something about Pete bred confidence, but at the same time, there was a petulance, which meant you always expected the unexpected.

Looking at Peter Hain and David. "The source confirms the 'Birthday Card' recently turned up in Belgrade."

'The Birthday card', was a euphemism we used for the missing warhead. Codes and secrets were the territory we moved in.

"Write the story and I will bring it up in the 'House'," Peter proclaimed decisively, taking a deep breath and holding everyone's gaze with his energy.

Publication and the question would be coordinated, which was standard practice in the world of secrets and spin.

Belgrade, a landlocked city, was known as the 'Powder Keg of Europe'. This euphemism described Belgrade perfectly; it had spawned many conflicts. When the 'Birthday Card' went missing the Balkans, conflict was raging. The Bosnians were besieged in Sarajevo, while Bosnian Serb leader Radovan Karadzic, self-styled poet-psychiatrist, former Bosnian Serb politician and President of the Serbo-Croatian Republika Srpska, was posturing and threatening.

Into the silence of the moment I offered, "Everyone knows about arms going to Iraq, but the trade through Yugoslavia is still more or less secret."

Pete nodded his head mentioning, "There is also Allivane supplying the fuse-line for Iraq's CBW (Chemical and Biological weapons) all going through Yugoslavia and helped by the State-owned armaments company SDPR."

Allivane, the Scottish armaments company which had played a pivotal role in allowing Serbia to develop the deadly arsenal of shells now raining down on Sarajevo. Both Allivane (later renamed Aero Technologies), together with Belgium based Space Research Corporation (SRC), Gerald Bulls, company, were conspicuously in breach of NATO guidelines. Of course, laws, embargos, right and wrong were for the public who funded all the bills, not for those who had the reins of power and profit in their hands.

The SDPR Serbians State owned Arms Company had played a part in funneling illegal shipments of arms to Iraq. For their part, the Serbians took a cut from each arms shipment travelling through their territory, amassing a huge stockpile or arms.

"The Serbs are now engaged in Ethnic Cleansing, but the Government favors the Serbs," Peter Hain said.

Tumbling from the ether came horrifying pictures of matchstick people clinging to wire fences and the animal-like screams of women and children being raped.

Sarajevo a European capital just a hop, skip and a jump from Bern and Brussels. Women and children were raped in their thousands; people were forced out of their homes and randomly shot. Karadzic gave orders to Serb snipers to shoot civilians in the streets.

Not since the devastation of the Third Reich had, Europe witnessed the horror of concentration camps. By design, the whole Slavic area was moving towards mass destruction and the, powers that be, had determined that no one would help the Bosnians.

"US officials are calling the conflict a 'problem from hell'. With Yugoslavia being used as an 'arms' conduit to Iraq, war in the region was an inevitable consequence," I said.

Pete Nodded, "It's an explosive mix," looking at each one of us in turn, "and the 'Birthday Card' is an unwelcome guest," he said.

"We need to get this out quickly," Hain interjected, passing a fleeting look at the door as if despite the radio churning out forgettable music someone might still be able to overhear.

Peter Hain had one of those stove hot, urgent personalities. You just knew you must pay attention, in case you missed what he said. His sense of urgency was so electric. I imagined a psychic in the future coming into the room, still being able to see our ethereal shapes deep in conversation.

Looking at David, I said, "With the Serbian's taking a cut of the arms going through their territory to Iraq, they have a stack of Bulls 155's Blaise Bleed munitions."

Pete sighed, saying, "There is also the matter of Bulls 600 mm guns which the Serbians have. It's possible they could be used as a launching system. The 1000mm Super-Gun was intended to launch an FOB[48]."

"I helped the Trade and Industry Select Committee investigate super-gun as you know," I said.[49]

Languishing in a chair, Pete turned his face to Peter Hain saying, "I'll send you a draft of the story, through Isobel, along with the publication date."

A vision of Isobel Larkin, Peter Hain's assistant, sprang to my mind. Isobel was a plump, pleasant round faced girl, I say, girl, because although she was no longer in the first flush her openness made her seem young. A committed Labour acolyte, she would later work for the Trades Union Congress (TUC). Her dark brown hair was cut just at the shoulder line. She radiated trustworthiness, streaked with the boring. Isobel would never be working for 'them' she was too open, too honest and too obvious to spot - I liked her. Isobel was not invited to the meeting but would be filled in on what happened later.

I was reminded that Hain, Pete and I were all birth sign Aquarians, all water bearers. They say the true Aquarian is a mix between genius

---

[48] Fractional orbital bomb.

[49] In the years following the arming of Saddam Hussein by the West these same Western Nations would falsely accuse Iraq of harboring WMD's (Weapons of Mass Destruction) as an excuse for the euphemistically named 'Operation Iraqi Freedom' invasion of Iraq in 2003. The policy to destabilize the oil- rich Middle East for personal profit would continue. Before this they had armed both Iraq and Iran to enflame the conflict and in 2015 they would arm Syrian 'Moderate Rebels' to overthrow the Syrian Government.

and madness. Sitting in that room with Hain and Pete I could feel both genius and madness at times intermingling, at other times separating. One moment I was touched by the genius and at other times, captured by the wild and crazy.

Just as my thoughts were drifting idly to the documents on the nearby table, all in a moment the meeting was over. As if, a drawbridge had risen from a moat cutting off all communication.

Together we strode out of the unknown MP's office, a group of conspirators ambling with forced nonchalance we entered a world where ears were everywhere. Somehow, the corridor looked bigger as if the cream walls dappled with spots of sunshine had grown.

Peter and David strolled with us to the top of the stairs, where we muttered our brief goodbyes. David's fresh face had a troubled look as we turned and walked down the stairs. I can still see his fair head tipped in goodbye with the shine of honesty making a halo around him. It was a year before I would see him again.

I said a quick goodbye to Peter Hain, who stood behind David like a sapling sheltering under a tree. They would talk when we had gone.

Down the stairs we went, I just a footfall behind Pete as he pushed open the door into the foyer. Ignoring the now cold gaze of the two policemen, we walked to the far doors silently as if preoccupied.

Once we had escaped from the Parliamentary building, we laughed together. Going over the scenes and finding the humor in the twists and turns. Something about the seriousness of these situations makes laughter inevitable. Releasing a dam of emotions into the twinkling happiness of friends sharing a joke. Looking at the sky, a wisp of a cloud hanging in the blue-silver vastness looked like a float of pink candyfloss. The world of conspiracies gave way to the joy of nature.

The following day we began work on the article for Business Age exposing the theft of one of the UK's nuclear warheads. Business Age Magazine was run by a colorful character Tom Rubython[50], whose

---

[50]   Tom Rubython later would stand as an MP for UKIP.

Teflon coated personality did not suffer the faint hearted. Once Tom had made Pete a director of one of his companies without telling him. However, as an Editor Tom was a dream, he never said never, and he did not ask a lawyer's opinion. With a desk drawer full of libel writs, he did not notice a new addition to the pile. All he asked was a good story for his readers. Tom knew how to put a magazine together; to this end, he hired the fearless and the gifted. This included writer extraordinaire Kevin Cahill, so well known for his 'Rich List.'

We had two projects at that time one about the 'Birthday Card', and the other would hit the world with the title 'When George Bush met James Guerin and what happened next.' The job of a researcher was painstaking in 1993, no internet for quick access to information. It relied on a lot of reading, trawling through company house records, sifting through the press cuttings and interviews as well as the dreaded microfiche reader. Of course, my research was complemented by inside-information, but that had to be checked-out.

Having been a financial journalist, Pete had a wonderful grasp of facts and could join many disparate parts of a story together with expertise. Cluttered with memorabilia from charity shops Pete lived in a first-floor apartment in Battersea, London. Someone had chosen the décor, maybe the previous tenant or maybe the landlord – it was drab. In the lounge, a two by three foot coffee table, which had once been a box of WW11 shells, took center stage while in the corner a naked ladies dress store dummy stood behind a small bar made in the shape of a boat. Strange and cluttered as the flat was, contrarily the office was a picture of efficiency, save for the mantelpiece littered with small pottery and soft animals and a few scatter cushions.

Pete sat down at his computer to write the 'Birthday Card' Story. Cups of coffee followed by much talking and checking the details. This story would make waves, very big waves. Once the bones of the story were completed, he printed the pages, gathering them into a group, much as a poker dealer would shuffle the cards.

"Where are the scissors?" He asked the silent room.

He looked to the left; I looked to the right. Kicking a red mottled cushion on the floor, I saw the scissors glinting under the light bulb. Grabbing them, he proceeded to cut the story into paragraph strips, and then placed them on the floor. The little pieces of paper clung desperately to the carpet pile as they were forced around. As the hours ticked by, the story manifested, perfectly collated each paragraph in its proper position like the stage at Covent Garden just before the Ballet is about to begin. The little pieces of paper reminded me of ballet dancers Tutus. I could almost feel the audience anticipation and hear the first strains of Tchaikovsky's Swan Lake, as dancers with sculpted faces and pink legs, under white froth gowns waited to begin. Pete and I were involved in another form of theatre, on a different stage, where risks were taken, and people lost their lives if they made the wrong step.

The phone rang, it was Isobel, able to hear only one side, I slumped in an easy chair and listened.

"Close to finish."

"Yes we can, you choose."

"Wednesday is fine."

"OK see you then," he finished, placing the cream receiver back into its waiting cradle.

"What did she say?"

"Wants to meet Wednesday in the Hotel bar."

"OK, that's fine before we do, we should run this whole thing past JJ, I will arrange a meet."

JJ was an extraordinary man, a senior intelligence officer he was responsible for many covert operations. He was both a mentor and a friend.

Never easy to arrange a meet without being watched and out of range of intrusive listening devices, we used the old staple, the British red telephone box. My lines were not secure, but the lines I called were extremely secure.

Putting on a dark dogtooth jacket, I placed a mustard brown silk scarf over my blonde hair and went to find a suitable phone box. The streets were busy with people enjoying the evening air. A youthful couple went passed hand in hand, an old man smoking a cigarette crawled along the pavement, wheezing as I overtook him. Walking I spotted a quiet square abundant with trees. In the corner, almost hidden under the spreading branches of an old Ash was a suitable telephone box. Checking up and down the street for surveillance, I stepped into the box, pulling the glass door closed behind me. The conversation was quick, to the point and over before, it began. We would meet the next afternoon in Hyde Park on a certain bench, where we had met before. No mention was made of the location, no mention of the bench just:

"I will meet you where we met before."

17 . FACT OR FICTION

The new day dawned bright and sunny but with a dampness that boded rain. Needing to check for tails and needing lunch, Pete and I made our way to Asda, Britain's Walmart. The fish and chip, plus peas, dinner was £1.99 including buttered bread and a cup of hot tea; no better value in London for a simple meal.

Dangling above the massive supermarket, Asda's restaurant was a big open room littered with naked vinyl tables, the type with those strange protruding edges in a dirty cream color. As you walked in you could see the whole room, which was bright due to the giant windows running down the length of one side. Day and night, the bulbs blazed against its cream roof.

A stack of green plastic trays stood at the entrance to a food counter cordoned off from the rest of the room by a twisted rope slung from waist high poles. Picking up a tray each, we sauntered along pushing the trays down the counters metal strips as we went. Using peripheral vision, I continued to scan the room for agents. Aware spies may already be in place, having been pre-warned we were going to Asda, I inspected each face or back for telltale signs. Not forgetting to watch for those people who arrived immediately after we did.

After being followed for years I had developed a sixth sense, and could spot an agent without even being able to see them. Agents and watchers have a certain primitive awareness, a certain aura an almost imperceptible smell of danger. In the field, your senses are honed to the point where you have a wolf's awareness. You can smell fear and sense danger. Today my senses told me everyone in the restaurant was innocuous.

Taking a table on the outer edge of the restaurant, we sat down to eat. Making sure, we faced the door, that way we could spot incoming danger. All the tables around us were empty, so it was safe to relax, eat and talk.

"Has to be the best value meal in town," Pete said, cutting into the battered fish.

"Must be," I said. "Have you heard from Machon, or has his battleship arrived?"

"He phoned me the other day. Talking about you," Pete went on, with a hint of laughter wrinkling the skin around his eyes. "They haven't told him we're close friends, it's funny.

"Every time he mentions you he talks about what you said about the CIA."

We both started to laugh, which made eating difficult. A chip spun off the plate and landed at my feet on the cream and grey tiled floor.

"He said to me..." Pete paused, while he searched his repertoire for a Glasgow accent. "Ye know what she said to me Pete; she said I can tell the CIA because they wear Ray-Bans and have CIA written on their backs, that's fucking ridiculous, love horse eat grass."

We both collapsed into fits of laughter. I could almost hear Frank's raspy Glasgow accent. Frank loved to complain. Perhaps it was something to do with the life he led being the receptacle for so many secrets and always at risk.

Settling down from the laughter, I caught the whiff of danger. Behind us sat an agent. He had sneaked in while we were engrossed in tales of Glaswegian Frank. With a sharp intake of breath, I met Pete's eyes. He also noted the man; a bucket of cold water was thrown on our spirits. The man in his early forties was encased in an oversized dark brown coat. The coat had a ragged tear in the shiny brown lining, but his brown shoes were brightly polished and glinted under the light bulbs. Without success, he was attempting to look poor and inconspicuous. Viewing him obliquely, we finished our meal in silence, leaving without a second glance at the agent with the torn coat lining.

Hitting the street, the noisy bustle of Clapham Junction assaulted me. Watching for a black cab with its Hire sign lit up we wandered along, stopping to look in shop windows we had no interest in at all. The pavement was damp; it had drizzled while we were at lunch. Spotting a cab, we both moved to the side of the road flagging him down with an outreached hand. Pete opened the shiny black rear door, and I stepped inside.

"Where to Gov'?" The cabbie asked, in a splendid East End accent.

I heard a sharp twang as Pete closed the door behind me.

Going to the cabbies open window, he said, "Hyde Park Corner."

As the cab moved off into the flowing traffic, I caught a final glimpse of Pete disappearing into a nearby shop. He would deliver the finished story to Business Age for publication in the July '93 issue.

Reaching Hyde Park, I paid the driver. Stepping out of the cab the buzz of many car engines assaulted my ears. The drizzle had stopped, leaving a fresh smell of grass emanating from the park. Glancing around with a practiced eye, I checked for enemy agents. Then moved towards the inviting green space, sauntering along the slate gray path.

My eyes were drawn to the swinging coattails at the end of a long black cashmere coat, and the slow measured yet strident step of its wearer. I would have known that figure anywhere, even at this distance; he exuded an aura of supreme confidence. Continuing towards the receding figure, I spotted the spotters. Just like the movies, one walking a dog and another reading a newspaper. The thrill of the moment oozed from every pore. The excitement was palpable. An edge manifested like static in a thunderstorm and yet it felt safe.

Knowing a delay was sensible, I halted underneath a Chestnut tree in full bloom whose wide branches spread around like the skirt of a Spanish dancer. To the left, an agent with the sleek brindle dog noticed I had stopped. Reaching up, I fluffed out my hair from the trap of my coat collar, allowing locks to flow out over the topcoat buttons. Then walked on.

JJ was seated at the far end of a park bench I knew so well. Across his aristocratic yet craggy features, a slow hint of a smile appeared and just as quickly disappeared. Sitting down on the opposite end of the bench, we were just two strangers to any observer.

"What did Hain say?"

"He said he is going to bring up the 'birthday card' in the House," I answered.

With peripheral vision, I saw his immobile face set deftly into a caricature of seriousness.

"You would all be discredited if he did."

His words were like an assault. I had not considered the strategy dangerous, just exciting.

"Why?" I questioned, still absorbing the predicament.

"There are two possibilities here, one they will accept a nuke has been sold into a war zone by someone with access to Britain's Nuclear Deterrent making you and Hain heroes. Alternatively, the story is bullshit and Hain and you are idiots. Think about it, which of the two possibilities is more likely?"

Was I so impulsive, so reckless that I had missed the obvious.

"You're right, of course, it was a mistake."

"No mistake, turn everything to your advantage, see everything as an opportunity.

"The other consideration is the lines are still running to the Balkans, despite the embargo so it's out of bounds."

We had only been able to expose 'arms to Iraq' because the lines had closed down, he was right, they would not allow us to expose arms deals with the lines still running.

Controlled exposure was an 'Organization' specialty. Gathering evidence as they go, they arrange the logistics to deliver all the illegal arms to a country. The evidence is collated and saved for the latter purpose of controlled expose. Every order, delivery note and false end-user certificate, together with the names of the people involved, all documented and secured. When the lines are finally shut down, all the evidence is gathered together and professionally exposed. Piece by piece, document by document like a demolition expert preparing for the controlled explosion of a skyscraper. No one in the building escapes, and all those who are to be saved are pre-warned.

Part of the job was to expose those shady deals and those people no longer useful. Of course, I would have liked to blow the whole thing apart, but the risks were high. Perhaps on some forgettable street, my life would have ebbed away. JJ broke through my thoughts, with a voice like a knife through butter.

"My advice is to drop it."

The silence absorbed our reflections as if a black sheet absorbs sunlight. We sat perfectly still as if someone had pressed the video pause button. Nothing moved *time and space were illusions after all*. These were stolen moments never to be repeated.

"Be safe," he said, as he stood.

A flood of warmth hit me as if an angora blanket had dropped from the skies. Then he was gone like the sun behind a cloud. The enchantment broken, only the cacophony of bird song remained as a background to the reflection on his words.

Strolling back to the road, my mood dispelled when a child skipped passed, her blue, crème and brown coat flowing like reflections in the rain. Hailing a black cab, I slumped back with a bump into the world of city streets and takeaways.

Journeying back to Pete's apartment with my inner thoughts punctuated by the insistent traffic noise.

"Drop me here," I told the driver, who quickly drew the cab to a standstill. Seeing £8.80 displayed on the meter, I thrust £10 into his hands, "keep the change."

After walking past the few doorways to Pete's apartment building, I sat down on the small brick red wall leading to his front door. Mulling over the meeting with JJ. *Of course, he was right; it would only play into 'their' hands.* Hain must not raise the stolen nuke in the House. They were experts at the game of spin and with so many journos in their pay; it was a foregone conclusion who would win the battle of the stolen warhead. My enthusiasm to create a show had masked the obvious flaws. We had to stop Hain from raising it.

There was a lonely red telephone box not far away. Dragging open, the glass door I stepped inside.

"Is Pete Sawyer there?" I asked the girl on the Business Age News Desk.

I waited, reading the adverts stuffed inside the glass-framed panel with the telephone operating instructions. - Masseur private treatment ring, the pretty boy, seeks similar.

"Hello," it was Pete.

"Check the meeting with Isobel is definitely on for tomorrow, we need to talk to her urgently," I said.

"Ok," he said, "I will be back in 30 mins. Meet me in The Fox and Hounds."

Putting the battered black receiver down, I noticed a watcher on the opposite side of the road. He had an anxious air as if he did not want to be standing there. These 'Five' (MI5) types were told to keep targets under surveillance but not told why. Something had spooked him. Hearing the throb of an engine, I turned to see a black car with tinted windows parked on the side of the road. The watchers, were being watched. *Taxpayers money being wasted again on intelligence gathering to save the skins of the few corrupt, dissolute, elite, shady businessmen, politicians, and intelligence chiefs.*

Leaving the red box, I strode the short distance to The Fox and Hounds, which is a typical London pub. Still early so not filled with smoke or incessant rock music. Walking to the window, I squeezed onto the bench, of an empty table with a clear view of the street. Settling down to wait I retrieved a dog-eared copy of the Art of War by Sun Tzu from my old brown bag and began to read.

Pete arrived in a flurry. Spotting me he waved, he had an uncanny knack of always knowing where people were. Buying a half of lager and a packet of salt and vinegar crisps, he trundled over and sat down. His unruly straight black hair was shadowing his eyes as he tore open the crisp packet offering me one golden crunchy morsel.

Taking the crisp, I said, "JJ says if Hain brings this up in parliament, it will discredit us all. Clearly we need to change our strategy."

His eyes locked with mine as he took in the information and assessed it. After a long pause, while he appeared to be inspecting his glass, but wasn't, he said.

"He may well be right. We were too keen on the chase."

"OK, let's talk to Isobel tomorrow and see what can be done."

From the wide, bright street, I entered the modern hotel foyer, a large open space with a long high desk to the right. A girl in a dark business suit, stood behind a desk talking to a man in a dark business suit. Their gray similarity suggested the same hotel tailor. Amongst the antiseptic furniture, no guests were visible.

The bar was upstairs, and I decided to walk rather than take the lift. Entering the bar, it thronged with customers, downstairs the Hotel had seemed empty, but the bar upstairs was buzzing with life. Soft classical music drifted around giving an atmosphere of elegance. Succumbing to its charm I held my head aloft, straightening my shoulders, the silk blouse clung to the warm skin beneath my jacket.

To the right, with sunlight streaking over her back was Isobel, reliable as ever, her cherub like legs crammed under the table. A plain girl dressed in black and white she could have been so easily missed except that she was under intense scrutiny. Even the watchers, watching the watchers, were being watched. Reading the pink pages of the financial times, a man in his fifties elegantly and expensively dressed, appeared immersed in the newspaper. Too classy for 'five' (MI5) he was definitely 'six' (MI6). A handsome middle-aged couple were watching both him and me, and Isobel. At the bar lounged the arrogant, know nothing MI5 agent, always so easy to spot.

Sauntering over to Isobel I passed the 'six' officer, for a brief moment in time I glanced down, otherwise motionless he raised his eyes over the paper to lock with mine. He knew, and I knew, and there was no problem. Behind me, there was a kafuffle as Pete came rushing through the door and sidled up to me.

"Sorry late, the tubes," he muttered matching my pace.

We both arrived at Isobel's table and sat down opposite her on the mottled brown upholstered chairs.

"Hello, Isobel," Pete said.

Our greetings were quickly over. This was not a social meeting.

Isobel began directing her question to Pete, "Peter Hain is anxious to raise this matter, when will the story be published?"

Pete leaned back in his chair in a languished manner, belying the troubled thoughts racing through his head.

Raising his eyes to Isobel's, "There is a slight problem there Isobel."

He hesitated, looking for the right words, "We have word that it would be a mistake for him to raise this…, maybe even a big mistake," he said.

Isobel raised her eyebrows in surprise, "I thought everything had been worked out?"

Pete smiled using his charm to quiet her, "Yes, yes it had, but we have good advice it will not go well."

Tiny wrinkles furrowed her brow and her lips slightly pouted, "He won't like this he is very insistent, really committed to raising it."

Looking at her I said, "In the end, it's up to him Isobel, the story will be published, but it's better if you can dissuade him. We have intelligence that the fallout would be bad for his career, they will use spin and press lapdogs to discredit the story."

Her intelligent eyes took in that possibility and strength and determination replaced her wavering.

"Somehow I will get him to listen…" she went silent for a moment, "When will it be published?"

"In the July edition, so there is plenty of time to dissuade him from raising it," Pete reassured her.

The persistent telephone ring stole into my dreams. It was the middle of the night. An owl hooted in the square opposite, as the phone continued to break the peace of sleep. Turning over did not work, burying my head under the pillow merely stifled the clamor of the bell. Placing my bare feet on the cool parquet flooring, I stumbled out into the hall where the offending phone just rang and rang.

"Hello," I mumbled, still half asleep.

"Tara?"

"Yes."

It was Peter Hain

"Give me a good reason to back off."

"It could ruin your career."

"Okay- Goodnight."

The phone went dead. Mission accomplished the Birthday card story would appear on the pages of Tom Rubythons, Business Age Magazine, as a humble apologue.

In July, the story ran headlined 'Fact or Fiction: Did a British Nuclear Warhead end up in Serbia?' I collected an early copy the pictures of the soldiers guarding the nuclear convoy came out well.

The Ministry of Defense (MOD) complained about the photographs of the nuclear convoy, but no one took any notice. Then the Court issued injunctions to prevent further publication and every copy of the magazine was gathered up and removed from the distributor's shelves. However, they were not complaining about Fact or Fiction it was our other story published in the same issue.

One of the most extraordinary stories around concerns the British nuclear warhead that may — or may not — be in Serbia. There is some evidence to suggest that the tale may be true.

Fact or Fiction: Did a British warhead end up in Serbia?

By Pete Sawyer

One of the most extraordinary claims contained within the mountains of written evidence sent in to the Scott Inquiry on arms for Iraq that a year ago, a British "nuclear device" was "stolen" from a road convoy while in transit from Coulport in Strathclyde to Burghfield in Berkshire.

As if that wasn't bad enough, it was claimed that the device somehow found its way to Belgrade, the Serbian capital.

This outrageous claim was made by a source who liaised closely with British intelligence during the Gulf War in 1991, but was understandably reluctant to be identified in this article.

To the Serbs such a weapon would be priceless. The political and diplomatic fallout for this country from such an incident – if found to be true – would be similarly difficult to quantify.

Considerable scepticism surrounds the claim. But other intelligence sources have since provided further details and confirmed that the incident took place. Maybe.

On July 16th last year, a Ministry of Defence convoy was supposed to be following a route from the Polaris submarine base at Coulport on the River Clyde, to the Atomic Weapons Establishment at Burghfield in Berkshire.

A mystery surrounds the convoy's precise cargo – described to *BusinessAge* as a "nuclear device". The most likely contender is a Chevaline – the warhead which sits on top of a submarine-launched Polaris missile. These are currently regularly transported from Coulport to Burghfield for dismantling as Polaris is phased out and gradually replaced by Trident.

The warheads are carried in specially adapted articulated lorries. Travelling with the lorries is an assortment of vans, coaches, escort vehicles, motorcyles, and a fire engine.

Greenpeace, deeply concerned about the safety of convoys carrying nuclear weapons, had taken a keen interest in these convoys – and in this convoy in particular. What adds to the mystery is the fact that the notes and details on the incident have vanished from Greenpeace's office. However, the environmental organisation's nuclear convoy specialist (whose identity is known to *BusinessAge* but not revealed for legal reasons) offered a first-hand account of events.

The convoy left Coulport on July 15th and had spent the night at Longtown near the Scottish border. That was where Greenpeace picked it up. Security at Longtown was unusually tight - even by normal standards. Around 120 armed police stood on guard at the Longtown base. Additional personnel had been specially brought up from York.

After a diversion supposedly arranged by the Ministry of Defence, Greenpeace

The mysterious breakdown... guarding against intruders.

lost the convoy for about five hours after it left Longtown early in the morning on 16th July. But one of Greenpeace's observers spotted the convoy mid-morning,

The nuclear weapon convoy...on the M62 near Junction 24.

heading south on the M6 between Carlisle and Penrith. A short while later it was seen on the A66 heading towards Scotch Corner near Darlington.

Greenpeace tried to catch up with the convoy had vanished. It remained elusive until the early afternoon when it was seen steaming along the M62 towards Leeds.

Just before 3pm, the convoy broke down for an hour. But the breakdown didn't fit the usual pattern for such events – leaving a suspicion that it may have been staged especially for Greenpeace.

That night, after a short diversion to RAF Finningly near Doncaster, the convoy eventually lumbered into RAF Wittering in Cambridgeshire, where it stayed put. Rather unusually, the convoy did not proceed on to Burghfield – suggesting that the warhead carrier was certainly empty by the time it reached RAF Wittering, if not for the entire journey.

Two days before the convoy set out from Coulport the Ministry of Defence published a report on the safety of British nuclear weapons which admitted that, during transport, such weapons are vulnerable to security threats and accidents.

So much for the convoy. What about the outrageous suggestion that this device was bound for Serbia?

Britain has a surprisingly long history of helping Serbia out. During the Second World War the Serbian government-in-exile was based in London. The Special Operations Executive – the precursor of MI6 – gave covert support from its station in Cairo to Serb Chetniks engaged in guerilla warfare against the occupying German forces.

More recently, the Serbian part of Yugoslavia has helped us out, too. Arms companies such as Allivane, the Astra subsidiary PRB and the Space Research Corporation, the company run by Iraqi supergun designer Gerald Bull, all had offices in Belgrade.

Allivane helped equip what was then the Yugoslavian Federal Directorate of Supply and Procurement with an SRC-designed 155mm shell production line. In return for the technology transfer, Yugoslavia allowed Bull to set up a firing-range for advanced shells and howitzers. Allivane got cheap fuses.

Several former Allivane and SRC directors have confirmed that the former Yugoslavia was used to provide false end-user documentation for goods destined for Iraq. In "payment", Yugoslavia amassed a huge stockpile of weapons, including

155mm shells and howitzers that can outgun anything possessed by Nato. Some of the goods – including parts for a baby Supergun – were earmarked to Iraq but never quite made it.

Most of this weaponry is now in the hands of the Serbian forces.

We had been told by our mysterious contacts that the "stolen device" had taken three days to reach Belgrade, arriving on July 19th.

We were also told that, soon after the incident had taken place, the Foreign Office sent in an undercover team to try and retrieve the weapon. The Serbian desk at the Foreign Office were horrified to receive our call. Yet a few days later, they dismissed it all as just rumour.

The Ministry of Defence wouldn't discuss anything at all involving nuclear warhead convoys. The reason? They are quite rightly concerned that terrorists or other such unscrupulous people might use such information to attempt a theft of a nuclear weapon in transit...

All this leaves the case wide open. Such a "theft" – if it did ever occur – could go a long way towards explaining the West's curious stance over the Balkans and why no one wants to go anywhere near Serbia. Britain could be severely embarrassed over such an incident. America could have played that to her advantage.

As a strategy for reducing Britain's burgeoning national debt by selling a few nuclear weapons – Kazhakstan-style – it is fatally flawed. Worse still, the decision to carry out such an operation, if indeed it ever occurred, must have been taken at very high levels, by someone who was clearly reckless or insane, or possibly both.

But then, looking at the sort of educational toys Britain and the West gave Saddam Hussein to play with, anything is possible.

The convoy...before the breakdown on the M62.

18. SHOPPING LIST

"For we are opposed around the world by a monolithic and ruthless conspiracy that relies primarily on covert means for expanding its sphere of influence--on infiltration instead of invasion, on subversion instead of elections, on intimidation instead of free choice, on guerrillas by night instead of armies by day. It is a system which has conscripted vast human and material resources into the building of a tightly knit, highly efficient machine that combines military, diplomatic, intelligence, economic, scientific and political operations." John F Kennedy 1961

George Bush Senior was a major player in the illegal arming of Iraq. He objected to our article, 'When George Bush met James Guerin and what happened next', which appeared in the same issue of Business Age Magazine as the story about the Missing warhead.

James Hartley an arms dealer and Sara Keays, the former Mistress of Defense Minister Cecil Parkinson, took their objections to the odious class ridden UK libel Courts. While Sir David Checketts, who had been equerry to both Prince Charles and the queens consort the Duke of Edinburgh, threatened to sue us. I dare not say more.

The day after the article appeared I traveled to London from North Wales by train, leaving the car at Bangor Station. My numbered ticket which was for the aisle seat but I sat in the window seat out of preference. Opposite me, over the plastic table stuck between the seats, sat a middle-aged pair from a friendly agency, who always sent watchers out in couples. One row down to my left and facing me

INVESTIGATION

Allivane is a curious, small, defunct company that few have ever heard of. But it played a huge role in a scandal that reached to the heart of British and American governments.

When George Bush met James Guerin – and what happened next

By Pete Sawyer

For six years throughout the Iran-Iraq war a Scottish company called Allivane operated at the heart of the worldwide weapon sales business. Its role was sinister and its legitimate turnover around £2 million a year. In truth it was the conduit for bil-

lions of pounds worth of weapons deals which no one wanted to explain. Allivane kept both sides in the Iran-Iraq war topped-up with weaponry and 155mm shells throughout the 1980s – with the tacit support of sections of both the British and American governments.

The story is amazing – but then, so is the whole weapons business.

Allivane's history is intimately wrapped up with that of the US defence company International Signal & Control, its British purchaser Ferranti and the immensely fraudulent Bank of Credit and Commerce International.

In this country the blazes of publicity surrounding armaments companies SRC (Supergun), Ordnance Technologies, Rexon and Matrix-Churchill have done much to obscure Alli-

vane's crucial role. All of these affairs have their roots buried in Allivane deals. And during the late 1980s Allivane's name consistently appeared on the fringes of other covert arms scandals in France, Austria and Holland.

But to understand how Allivane came into being and why it is so important it is necessary to go back to 1976 – to a candid meeting on a long-haul flight between Hong Kong and Los Angeles.

The following account of that meeting and subsequent events has never before been told. It is based on documentary evidence and hundreds of hours of interviews with former Allivane and ISC insiders. It is as accurate as the nature of the weapons business will allow.

The meeting in question was between George Bush, later to become US President but then Nixon's envoy in China, and James Guerin, the founder of the US defence company ISC. Bush and Guerin found they could do business together.

A couple of years later, following extensive congressional investigations, a clean-up of the CIA was ordered – plus a complete shut-down of covert arms routes then running to South Africa, Israel, Lebanon, Pakistan and Iran. By then, Bush had risen to become head of the CIA.

But the routes were not shut down. They were simply handed on to Guerin by Bush to be run on a "plausible deniability" basis. However, partly because of the pro-Israel lobby on Capitol Hill, the routes could no longer operate from America. They needed a country with a far greater sense of secrecy.

So the CIA turned to Britain, which was then in the grip of a major balance of payments crisis with a prime minister, James Callaghan, who was in desperate need of petrodollars. This was an offer which, at the time, the UK simply could not afford to refuse.

In effect, Britain agreed to become the "patsy" for the CIA's dirty paperwork. It is surely no small coincidence that the then prime minister, James Callaghan, later became an advisor to BCCI.

That agreement marked the small beginnings of the largest covert weapons supply and destabilisation operation the world had ever seen. The Iran-Iraq war and the Lebanon conflict set the Middle and Near East on fire for more than a decade, generating billions of pounds of profits for the West. And it was to ultimately lead to Iraqgate – the first truly global political scandal.

According to evidence submitted to the Scott Inquiry now investigating the whole affair, the British and American sides of

James Guerin...a fraudster residing at a US penitentiary

sat a man in an expensive pinstriped suit, connected to him was a soldier in civvies patrolling the aisles. He sauntered up and down the carriage. To conserve energy I slept, awakening when the train came to a stop at Crewe Station.

A businessman with a briefcase boarded and now stood in front of me waving his ticket.

178

"That is my seat," he said, belligerently indicating the window seat I occupied.

I just ignored his ridiculous hostility over a train seat. The agents opposite me also ignored him. He may not have spoken at all. Our attitude infuriated him; color began to tinge his soft clean-shaven white face. However, he was at a loss what to do. He sat down, slamming his briefcase onto the table in front of him and glowered at me. Drifting again into sleep I awoke when the train came to an abrupt stop.

"Please remain seated, there is a suspected terrorist attack in the Station and we are waiting until it is clear."

We had halted outside of London on an empty track.

The man in the pinstriped suit and I locked eyes from across the train as the soldier in civvies came up to him and whispered in his ear. The businessman next to me sat bolt upright. He had caught the glance between the man in the expensive suit and me; he had seen the solider in civvies – he had walked into a nightmare. Now he understood why everyone had ignored him and he was terrified.

Picking up my bag, I said, "Excuse me," and walked to the rear of the carriage where some spare seats were available next to the doors. The soldier came and sat next to me.

They managed to remove any danger from London's Euston Station, and I was on my way to a meeting with Pete and some Banker from Deutsche Bank who told us, "They are not going to kill you."

In the world of mirrors, there are players and everyone else. The players can be found in any position or situation from cleaning the toilets to running a country. In the end, they are all pawns in the game.

A month later the Bosnian Serb leader Radovan Karadzic threatened Europe with nuclear strikes if the West ordered a military intervention in the Balkan conflict. The Austrian newspaper, Der Standard, quoted The Bosnian Serb leader as proclaiming that Serbs could acquire nuclear weapons and they would be prepared to use them.

"We are not prepared to give up our own self-defense. It is no problem to buy nuclear weapons on the world market. We will really carry it through. We have nothing to lose."

Der Standard quoted him as saying.

Several UK and USA papers featured the threat anecdotally. As the world laughed at his threats, those who knew about the 'birthday card' did not find his threats so amusing, nor his mere stance posturing.[51] Time would tell, dust would settle as the clockwork toy of a world kept on moving.

As the year advanced and summer turned into autumn, we forgot about the 'birthday card'. Then one chilly day a small group of Bosnians, operating in exile contacted us. Stationed in London they were fighting to change the prevailing NATO attitude to the terror and carnage stalking their homeland. The Bosnians complained about the failure to stop the ethnic cleansing, the concentration camps and the massacre of hundreds of thousands of civilians. Their plight was desperate, and winter was approaching.

President Clinton had entered the White House around the same time the Warhead had gone missing from Coulport. He sent Secretary of State Warren Christopher to talk with Russia and the major NATO allies, seeking to obtain support for a 'lift and strike' strategy in Bosnia. The Russians and NATO wanted to the let the Bosnians die. They had no interest in armed intervention, and the elite who had armed Iraq and Iran were disassociating themselves. The Serbs had been their trading partners in a deadly covert arms game, so they closed their eyes and ears and looked the other way muttering platitudes. They favored the Serbs.

In January 1994 General Mike Rose, an oddly delicate name for a military General was appointed the head of the Peace keeping troops in Bosnia.

Mike Rose was vaguely known to me because I of insiders who

---

[51] Karadzic was convicted of War Crimes in 2016
https://www.theguardian.com/world/2016/mar/24/radovan-karadzic-criminally-responsible-for-genocide-at-srebenica

knew him when he was head of the Special Air Service (SAS). He had, I was told been Clive's superior officer. Mike Rose had been the operations officer on the ground during the, now famous, storming of the Iranian Embassy back in 1980, Clive was one of the boys. Gunmen had taken and were holding hostages in the Iranian embassy when two SAS teams, the red team and the black team, stormed the Embassy saving the hostages and executing every alleged terrorist on orders from above. Since then Mike and Clive had taken separate routes, Mike, now General Rose climbed to a public position, while Clive had assumed his role in the world of secrets.

In July 1995 General Mike Rose was attempting to keep a grip on the Balkan conflict when the Srebrenica massacre of over 8000 Bosnian men and boys took place. Srebrenica was under UN protection and was declared by the UN as 'a safe area,' this had not stopped the Serb Army Republika Srpska (VRS) from capturing Srebrenica and massacring the inhabitants.

The Bosnian Serbs were in a good position. They had arms stockpiles. For every illegal shipment of, Arms to Iraq, going through Serb territory, they took a cut. The Bosnians, on the other hand, despite a failed arms embargo, we are running short of everything they needed.

The Srebrenica massacre changed the state of play, 8000 men and boys were too significant a number for the world to ignore.

The London Bosnian group asked someone to meet with them, and Pete went alone and in secret. Waiting in Pete's apartment for his return, I spent time researching an arms company named Seacomsar. This company was part of the structure of offshore companies and bank accounts, which always stood behind the covert shipment of arms and the inevitable backhanders that went hand in glove with them.

Hearing the soft rumble of a key turning in the lock in the hallway, I strained to listen. The relaxed as I recognized the familiar sound of Pete's footfall. Striding into the room. Pete threw a reporter's notebook down on the table. It dislodged the papers, causing two to tumble onto the floor.

"What's this?" I said, pointing at the notebook now in the middle of the papers.

"It's a shopping list," Pete said, slumping down in a black leather easy chair under the window.

"The Bosnians are in a bad position and desperate. They need arms, heavy arms, small arms and ammo, troop carriers…"

Picking up the notebook, I turned over the blue and white cover scanning the handwritten list. It was a shopping list of arms and equipment including ambulances, which was an arms dealer's euphemism for troop carriers. Putting the notebook down I watched as the cover closed over the shopping list.

"These are all American arms. We can't supply them," I said, with regret.

"I know," Pete said, pushing his straight resolute black hair off his forehead where it immediately returned still looking like a fringe.

We both looked at each other and in a split second said together, "Let's call Ronald."

Ronald was a good friend, an arms dealer and an extraordinary man with the best connections. Small of stature and much overweight, he rolled rather than walked. Ronald was a powerhouse his fierce spirit shone through everything he did. Pete picked up the phone, and I dialed his private number in Washington DC and put it on the loudspeaker.

"Hi Ronald, How are you?" Pete said.

"Hi, what's happening?"

"Just had a meeting with the Bosnians here in London, their situation is desperate," Pete explained.

"The war is a bloody mess, and no-one will help them. They've given me a shopping list, but it is all US stuff so we can't supply it."

"Fax it to me. I will see what I can do," Ronald said, his soft dulcet tones like honey poured down the handset.

"Ok, will send it in 5 mins or so."

Scrawling 5% on a piece of paper, I flourished it under Pete's nose. Glancing at the paper his eyes flashed me an 'OK'.

"Our fee is 5%." Pete said phlegmatically, replacing the receiver with a smile on his face.

Taking a crisp, unblemished sheet of white copier paper from the desk drawer, Pete copied the shopping-list from his notebook. He wrote all in capitals with a neat, quick hand used to taking notes in during hurried interviews.

"Is it ready?" I asked.

"One minute," he said, as he finished the last item, then handed me the list.

Placing the white sheet on the fax tray, I dialed Ronald's number. We watched as the paper slowly moved against the roller, until the message was gone, to reappear on the other side of the pond.

Five minutes or so later, the phone rang. Picking up the phone, Pete pressed the Loudspeaker button.

"I will pass it up." Ronald said without a hint of emotion.

The line went dead.

The Bosnians continued to suffer, poorly armed, they were defenseless against a well-supplied enemy. As the next couple of weeks drifted by the Bosnian, shopping list was forgotten.

Then one evening while doing some digging for the Scot Inquiry into Arms to Iraq, the telephone rang. Picking it up, Ronald's rushed voice said

"Watch the news."

As the line went dead, I reached over and turned on ITV news. Mike Rose was complaining about the Americans; they had ordered the UN out of Sarajevo airport, cordoned it off and landed their planes. No explanation, no warning and no one knew what they were doing. *Ah! The shopping list had been delivered.'*

The conflict took a turn in the Bosnians favor, and those supporting the Serbs ethnic cleansing were forced reassess their position.[52]

The smell of freshly roasted coffee wafted around the busy coffee shop in Victoria Station. The table positioned just outside gave me a perfect view of the hustle and bustle. It was interesting listening to the air chuffing of trains, the shuffle of many feet and the insistent, loudspeakers, "now standing at platform ten ...,"

Pete came striding over through the crowd. His exquisite tailored knee-length gray French cashmere coat hit me in the eye. No one would guess it cost £3 from a Clapham Junction charity shop, which somehow acquired all the clothes left behind in the underground.

"Just getting the coffee," he said, going to stand in line.

Placing two steaming cups on the table, the white froth of the coffee straining against the rims with a fleck or two cascading down the cream porcelain.

"The Bosnians called; very happy, everything was delivered, except the ambulances," he said.

"Despite no troop carriers, oops, I mean ambulances."

We smiled at each other.

"It looks like the war has turned and the 'problem from hell' has been solved." [53]

Pete took a sip of his coffee, a fragment of froth remaining on his upper lip.

"But what about the 'Birthday Card'?" He said.

---

[52] 'What, then, explains the Clinton administration's decision in August 1995 at long last to intervene decisively in Bosnia?'
https://www.brookings.edu/articles/decision-to-intervene-how-the-war-in-bosnia-ended/

[53] Four months later on December 14th 1995 the war ended.
https://www.brookings.edu/articles/decision-to-intervene-how-the-war-in-bosnia-ended/

19. WHAT A SCALLYWAG

"The very word "secrecy" is repugnant in a free and open society; and we are as a people inherently and historically opposed to secret societies, to secret oaths and to secret proceedings. We decided long ago that the dangers of excessive and unwarranted concealment of pertinent facts far outweighed the dangers which are cited to justify." John F Kennedy

The entrance hall to the Royal Courts of Justice, Temple, London, is an edifice of towering pillars of dressed stone. A Victorian building in the gothic style with corridors, alcoves, anterooms by the hundreds, worn stone floors and old courts lined with dark seasoned wood. Jurisprudence in Britain was born from the Templar spirit of justice but devolved into the habitation of servants for the dissolute rich and powerful. The Masonic Brotherhood is deeply ensconced in every area of the legal process. The Masons took on the Templars mantle of power, but not their vision, their strength or their love of truth.

Today in Court 13, a libel trial was coming to a close. The jury would deliver their verdict. It was December 1994, and for the past few weeks, it had slumbered on in front of Freemason Judge Sir Maurice Drake. Drake had declared he was a Mason at the start of the trial as the plaintiff was also a Mason. Instead of recusing himself, Drake carried on as if a common brotherhood with one party was a mere irrelevance. It was a jury trial, and Drake was conveniently in charge of the civil jury list.

The defendants were The Observer, The Independent on Sunday, Private Eye magazine and HTV, (Welsh Independent Television). The plaintiff was retired North Wales Police Chief Superintendent Gordon Anglesea, with his costs funded fully by The Police Federation.

Anglesea's name was passed to me as a pedophile in 1989 along with another nineteen police officers. Journalists and politicians trying to expose the pedophile cover-up in North Wales agreed, CSP Anglesea, was key to unlocking the on-going child abuse cover-up.

The Barrister for the defendants was George Carman QC and for the plaintiff Anglesea, Labour Politician from North Wales, Lord Mostyn Williams. Neil Kinnock recently made Williams a peer of the realm.

These illustrious participants, however, were mere bit actors. The real players were the young men, raped and abused by the plaintiff when they were children in State Care.

Williams was there to support the indefensible, the sexual abuse of vulnerable children in State care by a senior police officer. At the start of the Trial, he said:

> "They say he sexually abused them and being a serving senior police officer, abused his power in that rank. I clearly say those are the filthiest lies you can tell about anyone."

The battle lines were drawn. Truth stood in the dock while the forces of darkness gathered around to not only blindfold but also mortally wound her. What had led to this battle between the Police Federation and the Independent Media?

It started in North Wales with meetings in pubs between HTV, London Journalists and Politicians like Dennis Parry leader of Clwyd Council. The objective was to expose the on-going child abuse cover-up and call for a public inquiry.[54]

The crusade for a Public Inquiry was unpopular with the Home Office, the Police, the pedophiles and the crooks who made fortunes out of child trafficking. Journalists and investigators experienced being

---

[54] Early day motion in Parliament 686 calling for a Public Inquiry
http://www.parliament.uk/edm/1995-96/686

followed, burgled and threatened. It was dangerous to expose State sanctioned child abuse.

The Independent on Sunday first broke the story in December 1991 but did not name Anglesea. The story ran identifying a senior North Wales Police officer as a child abuser. Anglesea complained to the Paper, but they refused to apologize.

Following this, Scallywag Magazine, The Observer, HTV and Private Eye Magazine exposed the story. While the Independent and the Observer did not name Anglesea, Private Eye and Scallywag did.

Anglesea's legal team and the Police Federation had a special fate lined up for Scallywags editor Simon Regan. They planned to Jail him for criminal libel.[55] Scallywag's lawyer David Price was brought in to defend Scallywag.

Price was a young man who I often met in the Law Courts in London. He had a fertile legal brain, rarely buttoned his jacket and was always in a rush. He thought quickly, talked quickly, moved quickly and always made his point in a whirl of activity. He was also brave. Anglesea's solicitor Barton Taylor, of Russell Jones & Walker, said of Scallywag:

> "There is no purpose in claiming damages for civil libel against Scallywag because they consistently claim they have no money. Criminal libel is the only remedy against this worthless organization who simply seek publicity for themselves. They are not interested in accuracy, even less in fair reporting and are a disgrace to the profession of journalism."

The previous year Scallywag paid damages for defamation to serving Prime Minister John Major and therefore had suffered financial damage.

Rumors had been circulating in Fleet Street and Parliament

---

[55] David Price & Co has issued the writ on behalf of Scallywag. Barton Taylor says the magazine's writ will be robustly defended and fellow partner Sarah Webb and Andrew Caldecott QC had been instructed. The criminal libel proceedings against the magazine could follow Anglesea's action.

about the Prime Minister and a sordid extramarital affair.[56] To scotch these rumors and ruin Scallywag MI5 and John Major cooked up a dirty plan. They leaked the name of the wrong woman, Claire Latimer[57], to Scallywag. Journalists that are more cautious may have hesitated, but Scallywags editors Simon and Angus had not earned their reputations for fearless reporting for nothing, they published and paid the price.

Scallywag was publishing articles about the Westminster Pedophile Ring and the traffic of children from North Wales to London so Tory MP's could abuse them.[58] John Major and his Government wanted to stop the publication of the stories. They had the knives out for Scallywag's editors, contributors and researchers. The Anglesea libel trial, now ending was designed to be another nail in Scallywags coffin.

Waiting in the corridor outside Court 13. I could not bear to witness the young men who had described their multiple rapes and abuse be branded as liars, just as they had when, as children, they pleaded for protection.

Judge Drake had warned the jury:

"And of course a complaint that someone has sexually

---

[56] Later when the affair with Edwina Curry became public knowledge Scallywag's Lawyers, David Price considered Legal Action against John Major. http://www.dailymail.co.uk/news/article-140434/Magazine-threatens-legal-action-Major.html

[57] Claire Latimer was wrongly named as the adulteress is sure John Major used her as a decoy to draw attention away from his adultery with Edwina Curry.Later when Major's affair with Edwina Curry became public knowledge Scallywag's Lawyers, David Price considered Legal Action against John Major. http://www.dailymail.co.uk/news/article-140434/Magazine-threatens-legal-action-Major.html

[58] During 2012-2016 stories of a Westminster Pedophile Ring hit the headlines around the world. Sir Peter Morrison, Sir Leon Britten QC, Greville Janner, QC, Sir Cyril Smith, all being named. People noted the closeness to Scallywag Magazine's 90's articles. Scallywag Magazine rose, phoenix like, from the ashes, having a healthy new following. More people read the old articles than in its heyday back in the 90's

assaulted you is comparatively easy to make up and difficult to rebut. It is the nature of a sexual complaint that no one else is likely to have seen it."

The old court door swung open and Simon came out dark hair covering his burning tears. He did not notice me, standing like a shadow dressed in a black court suit, or notice my tears and clenched fists.

The jury, handpicked by Drake, awarded pedophile former Chief Superintendent Gordon Anglesea compensation of £375,000. The Court also guaranteed Anglesea its protection, ordering undertakings from the defendants to prevent further publication of the truth. The defendants were also ordered to pay all the substantial legal costs of the action.[59]

Simon Regan wrote:

"I watched it in the now-famous Court 13 at the High Court during the libel action between former Supt. Gordon Anglesey and Private Eye (and others) when despite the fact that under cross examination, Anglesey had to admit that his evidence did not correspond with his own notebooks, the 'other side' subsequently tore the five main witnesses to pieces in a monumental act of judicial harassment. Like the whole story of child abuse in North Wales and elsewhere, it broke my heart."

Two months after giving evidence against Gordon Anglesea, one of the young men Mark Humphreys, was found hanging from railings outside his bedsit in Wrexham. The North Wales Police said it was not suspicious.

The Courts had shackled the independent media, stories about children in State Care being raped and trafficked from North Wales, Islington, Lambeth, and Jersey would be spiked. Only Scallywag continued unabated.

---

[59] Former Chief Superintendent Gordon Anglesea sentenced to 12 years for child abuse in 2016 https://www.theguardian.com/uk-news/2016/nov/04/ex-police-chief-gordon-anglesea-jailed-child-sexual-abuse-north-wales

Enter Tory politician Dr. Julian Lewis. Taking advantage of a rent dispute Lewis purchased the contents of Scallywags offices, including the evidence against Westminster pedophiles. This was the final nail in Scallywags coffin.

Simon Regan wrote:

"Dr. Julian Lewis, now Conservative MP for New Forest (East) but then deputy head of research at Conservative

Central Office in Smith Square, managed to purchase the contents of our offices, which included all our files. It had been alleged that we owed rent, which we disputed, but under a court order, the landlords were able to change the locks and seize our assets, which included all our files, including those we had made on pedophiles. It was apparently quite legal, but it was most certainly a dirty trick."[60]

Scallywag was dead, but Spiked Magazine was born, founded and edited by Simon's half-brother Angus. One of the funders was Mohammed Al Fayed, the owner of Harrods.[61]

Spiked ran an article about the Pedophile Information Exchange (PIE) magazine MAGPIE, being published in the Home office. Another article explained how kids were used by MI5 to blackmail diplomats.[62]

I was researching and supplying information to Spiked, to push the Welsh Secretary William Hague to call a public Inquiry. In July 1996, we succeeded and the Government, reluctantly, announced The

---

[60] Julian Lewis explains how he was libeled as was CSP Gordon Anglesea and how he closed Scallywag down http://www.julianlewis.net/selected-news-coverage/3519:libelled-politicians-36

[61] Death of Princess Diana and Dodi Fayed. Were they going to Marry? https://www.express.co.uk/news/royal/847883/Princess-Diana-death-conspiracy-theory-engagement-Dodi-Al-Fayd

[62] Victim used by Mi5 and Mi6, trafficked from Kincora to London and Manchester https://villagemagazine.ie/index.php/2017/11/kincora-survivor/

Waterhouse Inquiry.[63]

Two private detectives employed by Al Fayed to dig the dirt on Tory Politicians offered Angus, secretly filmed, compromising photos. The pictures were of Defense Minister, Michael Portillo, engaged in sexual activity with an underage boy. The owner wanted £100,000 for the negatives. Al Fayed was not interested, so Angus went to Cyprus to get the money from fugitive tycoon Asil Nadir. Life was exciting.

September gave way to cooler days. While Angus was away in Cyprus, I was getting the low down on Michael Portillo MP and Johnathan Aitken MP for Spiked. Needing to check information, I decided to make a call. The rules were simple, ask the right questions and I would get the right answers, ask the wrong questions and end up with disinformation. Finding a lonely telephone box, I entered and dialed.

"Hello, it's Tara."

"Hello, how are you?"

"Angus from Spiked is in Cyprus making a deal with Nadir and-"

"Tara, Angus is dead."

"Dead," I said, the receiver slipping from my hand.

"He was in a car crash this morning," they have eliminated the threat."

"What about the photographs?"

"They will not surface; it's a bigger picture than you know."

"But-"

"Not now, it's the wrong time," he said.

---

[63] The Macur review of the Waterhouse Inquiry concluded that the masonic infiltration of the Tribunal was extensive
https://paddyfrench1.wordpress.com/2016/05/09/the-macur-review-part-one-bloody-whitewash/

I stood listening to the monotone of a dead line.

Angus James Wilson died that day. The photographs of Michael Portillo, the substantial check from Nadir and all Angus's possessions disappeared.

Simon Regan said that before Angus went to Cyprus,

"There was other wheeling and dealing in London prior to the Cyprus trip and I knew something big was impending. What it was in full is probably only known by Angus. All I know is that, prior to Angus going to Cyprus, Basham and Diamond had struck a deal and Angus was going to be the conduit. Basham's brief was to create a situation in which Nadir could return to the UK under 'benevolent' terms. That is that, at best, he is not charged at all and, at worst, the evidence against him is flimsy and he gets a token sentence."

With the death of Angus, Spiked died along with fearless investigative journalism. There were people as brave, as incorruptible and as resolute as Angus and Simon and I was to meet one. He was destined to become a legend in his own lifetime.

Shortly after Diana, Princess of Wales was slain in a Paris underpass I was preparing for a special guest. Honeybees, chubby brown and mellow yellow striped bodies hovered around the brilliant scarlet Azaleas on the patio. A white filigree metal table laden with cakes, sandwiches and orange juice blended into the black and white patio tiles. Two matching cushioned metal chairs were positioned around the table, giving a view over the massive lawn and on into the field and stretching out to the wooded horizon.

The preparations were for an extraordinary guest, a man of unusual perception, whose ability to see through the illusion caused the Secret State to launch a discrediting campaign against him. With remarkable composure, he bore the brunt of their attack, brushing it off like a duck skimming through a dirty lake brushes off the muddy water.

The sound of a vehicle drawing up cut through the gentle sound of buzzing bees. Going to the red gate, I flicked the metal catch as

David Icke stepped out of his car.

Opening the gate wide to invite him in, our eyes locked in an eternal gaze, which tore through time and illusion to an ineffable moment where universes were born and died with the breath. I saw his stars were fixed and he was destined to bring promethium fire to a dark world.

"Welcome David, please come in."

"Thanks."

Walking together to the patio, I noticed how big he was. We sat down together looking out, over the cakes and sandwiches, to the rolling countryside beyond. David breathed in its essence.

"It's a beautiful view," he said.

"Yes, I thought it would be a good place to relax and talk." Placing a plate in front of him, I said, "Please help yourself to the food. Would you like orange juice or I could make tea or coffee?"

"Orange juice will be fine."

Picking up the pitcher ice cubes crashed against the sides and the odd cube tumbled with the orange into his glass.

"I am researching for a book called 'The Biggest Secret', revolving around the secret agenda of the elite. It will go into the whole royal, pedophiliac and satanic configuration."

"That is a story which needs to be told. I have compiled a list of VIP British pedophiles, Sir Edward Heath, ex-Prime Minister is somewhere near the top."

"That name has come up before," he said, reaching out for a sandwich and placing it on his plate.

"Child procuring for sexual abuse and ritual abuse is the dark kernel at the heart of the rape of our planet and the enslavement of mankind," I said.

"Yes, creating fear, a frequency range vibrating to emotions of fear, guilt, resentment, aggression," he said, splaying out his fingers into the warm summer air. "The more, negative energy events they create on Earth, which generate fear, guilt, resentment, et cetera, the more in control they become. Every time we feel the emotion of fear, our thought-emotional patterns are sending out energy around and within us to the frequency of fear, which is all food to them."

"Yes, everything is energy, we mold it by our perceptions," I said, spreading my arms in a wide arc.

The bees had long returned to their hives and still we talked, shadows fell over the patio, then doused the garden in darkness until the stars sprung out of their dark blue cloak. On into the night, we traveled on the wings of our souls.

On November 4, 2016, Gordon Anglesea was finally convicted of child abuse and sentenced to 12 years in jail. He died in prison.

20. PROPAGANDA WARS

"If we let the propaganda wash away all truth from his death, we in some way lose our link to reality. State Murder is most heinous because by its nature it includes the complicity of the citizens. There can be no place for inaction or apathy when as a citizen; you have in part paid for the executioner. If we look on State murder as casual as or less interesting than a soap opera, we consign ourselves to live under unremitting oppression." Andrea Davison

Jill Dando was a star BBC presenter. Presenting a program called, Crime Watch, which focused on unsolved crimes. Jill was a clean, pretty blonde with a girl-next-door image.

Jimmy Savile was also a star presenter at the BBC, but he was the antipathy of Jill. Savile was a prolific pedophile and child procurer who had haunted the BBC abusing children for decades.

Savile a loud, rough, brutish Disc Jockey from a deprived area of Leeds was a close friend of the Royals, Politicians, the rich and famous. He had a special relationship with Prince Charles, and Prime Minister Margret Thatcher, spending time with them in their private residences. His relationship with the Royals was long standing, having been a friend of 'Tricky Dickie' Mountbatten, of Kincora fame, before the IRA blew him up.

The lives of Jill and Jimmy became tangled when Jill became aware of his child abuse on BBC premises and found out BBC equipment was being used to make child abuse images and videos. Jill joined a campaign to help children identify pedophiles and began to compile a dossier of evidence about abuse at the BBC to present to BBC bosses.[64]

Jill's celebrity status made her dangerous to the organization who runs the BBC as a ministry of disinformation. MI5 relied on the Beeb to prop up a system that protects the Establishment elite, so they vet everyone who works for the Ministry of disinformation.[65] Functioning as an unofficial arm of the State, citizens are compelled to pay for BBC propaganda in the form of a TV license, without which it is illegal for a citizen to watch TV.

Jill lived with her Medical Doctor fiancé Alan Farthing[66] in Cheswick London. She was selling her own house in Fulham London. One bright April day in 1999 Jill went to collect the post from her the empty house. She told only one person, Alan Farthing, but someone else knew she would be there alone. Jill walked across the black and white tiled porch to her front door with the house keys in her hand. From nowhere a man grabbed her from behind forcing her to her knees. In a single flowing, well practiced, movement he pushed her head down to the ground, pressed the silenced pistol to her head and pulled the trigger. The bullet passed from one side of her head to the other, landing in the tiny front garden next to a stunted, lonely tree. The assassin was a late thirties well-dressed tall white man and a professional killer with a military background. "Dando was a clear message to BBC employees to keep quiet," I was told.

---

[64] In August 2017 Liz MacKean mysteriously died suddenly. "Courageous investigative journalist and ex-BBC News correspondent Liz MacKean, 52, who exposed infamous pedophile Jimmy Saville – and ultimately resigned in 2013 over the BBC's decision to refuse to air her investigation into Saville – has died after suffering a stroke" https://www.thesun.co.uk/news/4276242/bbc-jimmy-savile-investigator-dies/

[65] BBC used MI5 to vet staff
http://www.telegraph.co.uk/news/uknews/1522875/Revealed-how-the-BBC-used-MI5-to-vet-thousands-of-staff.html

[66] Alan Farthing would later be made Gynecologist to the Queen. http://www.dailymail.co.uk/news/article-2244910/Why-murder-ex-fianc-Jill-Dando-haunts-man-deliver-Kate-Middletons-baby.html

When a familiar figure on TV or screen dies, there is an outpouring of public grief and those who plan these assassinations use this to prime the press. The first reporter on the scene was BBC reporter Clarence Mitchell, who two years earlier had covered the death of Princess Diana.

Jill executed by the State left Jimmy Savile free to procure and abuse more children. The Police soon had a patsy in mind to take the fall, a Fulham resident with a history of attention seeking and stalking, Barry George.[67]

State assassinations follow patterns depending on the urgency or the message to be delivered. Professionals with military backgrounds, used to murdering people in cold blood are used. They can be stage-managed operations as with Johnathan Moyal, James Rusbridger and Milligan or a clear and sharp message as with Gerald Bull and Jill Dando. Then there are wet jobs where a shot to the head will not do.

It was high summer in 2003. Sitting in the office engrossed in paperwork the phone rang. The display panel flashed number unknown; cautiously I picked up the receiver, but remained silent.

"Tara hello."

It was the distinctive Irish lilt of an ex-Mercenary working for MI6.

"Hello."

"We need to meet."

It was just days after the death of Chemical and Biological weapons (CBW) expert David Kelly, I guessed it was about the non-existent WMD's in Iraq.

"Is it important?" I said. "I'm swamped."

---

[67] George was convicted in July 2001 and given a life sentence. Few believed George was guilty. He appealed twice unsuccessfully. Then a third appeal succeeded after discredited forensics evidence was excluded from the prosecution's case. But the State made him go through a second trail where he was found innocent. To-date the State refuse to compensate George for wrongful imprisonment. https://google-law.blogspot.com.ar/search?q=jill+dando

Of course, I knew it would be important to them.

"Yes," he said, "remember the old place?"

"I do."

He paused, "Tonight at twenty-one, thirty."

"OK, I'll be there," I said, replacing the receiver.

Looking out of the office window over the Menai Straights the waters twinkled capturing the sun's rays and a swathe of green grass on the far side deepened in hue, as a cloud passed over the globe of the sun. The peaceful view belied my feelings. *The BBC outed David Kelly as their source. Now what did 'they' want with me.*

Right now, in Iraq, troops from the USA and UK risked their lives for a lie and hundreds of thousand innocent Iraqis would die for the same lie. David Kelly believed he could trust MI5 vetted BBC reporters when he disclosed the dossier used as an excuse to invade Iraq was sexed-up. He did not expect it to become news.

Five months earlier Blair's disinformation that Iraq had Weapons of Mass Destructions (WMD's) was used to justify the Second Gulf War. Even if Iraq had retained WMD's, which they had not, it would have been solely because the UK and USA had illegally supplied Iraq with the capability in the first place.

What was their problem with me, I thought looking down at the paperwork with its black printed letters, each one a symbol conveying a meaning, which now seemed to evade me. Visions rose of war and destruction, evil profiteers laughing as cities burned, and then salting away their ill-gotten gains in offshore bank accounts.

That evening during the waning moon, I drove along the Welsh country lanes. My British Racing Green MGF Abingdon, called Maggie, purred with a familiar hum as her lights illuminated the pebbled road ahead. *Should I be meeting on this lonely road.* Spotting the layby, I eased off the accelerator; it was at the corner of the dark lane big enough for two or three cars to rest.

He was already waiting; the sleek black bodywork of the Rover gleamed in Maggie's headlights for a moment until they went out as I turned off the ignition. The silence was oppressive. Getting out of Maggie I strode over to the Rovers passenger door and got inside. The new plastic seat clung to my coat for a second.

"Hello," I said, "what's happening?"

"Oh, we need to know your plans," he said, inclining his head towards me.

"About what?" I asked, unable to see his eyes in the dark.

"The WMD's."

"Me nothing, I am out of the game, I have not been asked to do anything on Iraq for a while."

"No, but you're on the list," he said.

"Look, everyone knows Iraq does not have WMD's it all went to Sudan, Libya and Iran, I have info about a mobile bio lab in the Iraqi Marshes, but it's small."

"Not everyone knows," he said, adjusting the windscreen mirror. "Your knowledge on the bio side is similar to someone else."

"You mean David Kelly?" I asked, lifting my eyes to his.

"My expertise is confined to logistics and weaponization."

"That makes you more dangerous, don't you think?"

"We're all dangerous John if you start taking out agents against the rules, soon no-one will be safe?"

"Well, we wouldn't want you to take a country stroll with painkillers," he threatened, or warned me; it was hard to tell which.

"So Kelly did not quite work out as a front man. Wasn't he due to retire?"

Tapping the steering wheel with his black-gloved hand, he said, "As for you?"

"Building up and then crushing Iraq is a crucial component of their strategy, I have no doubt they will go in."

"What about the viruses," he said.

Iraq had been supplied with large amounts of UK patented VX gas. A military industrial base, which included the facility to produce chemical and biological weapons and deliver them.

"The engineered viruses?" I asked.

"Well, that's your area and Kelly's," he said.

I knew how Dr. David Kelly had felt when he took his final fateful walk, he felt hounded and persecuted, so he went out into the countryside, to find a place away from the eyes, ears and hands.

Kelly had tumbled headlong into a Hitchcock movie, sensing eyes, ears and violating hands everywhere. Eyes reading his e-mails, ears listening to his conversations, hands stealing a document or a knife out of the drawer.

"You guys will not get authorization to take me out like Kelly," I said, looking at his averted profile.

David Kelly was a Welsh scientist specializing in Biological weapons. In 1984, he joined the civil service working at the most secret base at Porton Down[68], as head of the Defense Microbiology Division. He was also an adviser to the Ministry of Defense, the Foreign Office and MI6.

His theses 'The replication of some iridescent viruses in cell cultures' earned him an Oxford doctorate. He was ideally suited to investigate the bioengineered flu virus fired into Saudi onto allied forces during Desert Storm. He would understand the tech transfer and how the virus was transposed with a biotoxin. The secret State, would not want Joe Public finding out, how an engineered virus was piggybacked into the USA and UK via the Gulf Vets.

"There are other ways of silencing people," John said, breaking the silence with the precision of a chef slicing an onion. "What do you intend to do?"

"No mileage in this for me. Wait, watch, and follow events."

John was staring at me in that weird, with menaces, detached look of State assassins. Opening the Rovers door, I stepped out.

"I have no instructions, if that's what you mean," I said, as I closed the car door behind me with a resounding clank.

---

[68] Porton Down http://www.bbc.com/news/magazine-36606510

Walking towards Maggie, I pressed the electronic ignition key to see her welcoming headlights flash.[69]

As the year progressed, I began to tire quickly, and this steadily increased in severity until by 2006 I was sleeping almost twenty hours a day and could not walk up a flight of stairs without stopping to cling to the banisters. Then my hair started to fall out. Blood tests revealed a long-standing Thyroid problem. It would take years, I was told before I could lead a normal life. Certainly, I was no longer fit for front-line operations and did not present a threat to anyone.

One dark evening, as the full moon began to crawl into the sky to brighten the view from the office windows, the phone rang. Illness had robbed me of my sharp awareness. I wondered if I should just let it ring. It stopped, but stared again immediately. Someone knew I was at home. I picked up the receiver to hear a friendly voice from the past.

"Hello," he said.

"Hello, good to hear your voice."

"Your name has emerged on a list."

"What list?"

"The Duncroft list."

Involuntarily I let the phone fall to the table, I had not expected to hear that name; images of the small room where I was drugged and held in solitary confinement, appeared before me.

"Why?"

"It's Savile, his name is cropping up everywhere, but especially in

---

[69] Since that meeting, the UK Government convened the Hutton Inquiry headed by another pliant Judge which concluded against all the evidence that the government was right about the WMD's and Dr Kelly killed himself. http://news.bbc.co.uk/2/hi/uk_news/politics/3114489.stm. Then the Chilcot Inquiry concluded the opposite saying Iraq did not have WMD's. http://www.iraqinquiry.org.uk/media/247921/the-report-of-the-iraq-inquiry_executive-summary.pdf Both Inquiries were an unashamed media circus. Criminals who murdered hundreds of thousands of people in a fake war escaped with at most a slap on the wrist.

Haut de la Garenne and now in Duncroft."

"He's been involved with Duncroft runaways since the 60's."

"They are looking at him visiting the School."

"I don't remember that, but I was not there long. I absconded."

"The point is your name is on a list, and I'm telling you to take care. They will not let their special agent Jimmy go down, remember Jill Dando?"

"He's just one of the ring."

"But a Royal bosom buddy in possession of dark secrets. I'm just letting you know they will protect him at all costs."

For decades, the Security Services have been covering-up for an international group of pedophiles who traffic in children. Its big money and child procurers like Sir Jimmy Savile, are protected by the full power of the Establishment. He inhabited the halls of Westminster, was entertained in Thatcher's office and at her private retreat at Chequers He flaunted his close friendship with Prince Charles and was a confidant of the Royal family. With his links to the Vatican, Israel, MI6, and MI5, he was untouchable.

"Right now, I'm not strong enough to do anything much, other than write reports."

"Just saying, be careful and watch your back."

"Thank you so very much for the warning. I don't think I'm in any danger," I said, replacing the receiver with a quick goodbye.

For decades, I gathered documents and information about VIP and State child abuse, focusing mainly on the abuse of kids from children's homes. This evidence, which included Jimmy Savile, lay in the attic gathering dust.

Early one morning a loud and insistent hammering disturbed my sleep. Opening my eyes, the morning light spilled down from the skylight in the attic bedroom as my ears caught the sound of battering downstairs at the front of the house. The clock read 7.30 am, *who would be banging on the door at this time.*

Picking up the fluffy white dressing gown, I slipped it on over my pink nightdress and rushed downstairs. Drawing back the curtain edge covering the first-floor lounge window I peeped out. Ten or so hefty, rough looking men in wooly hats loitered outside in the front yard. My first instinct was to get the AR 15. A 20 round magazine was enough to take them all down quickly. Even with a straight pull rifle, I was fast. The image of a five foot nothing old lady in her pink nighty with an AR 15 shooting dead ten or so burly thugs was such a funny thought it cleared my mind. *Ten dead bodies in the main street would be too much for the cleaners to deal with.*

But I could escape over the flat roof from the shared office at the rear of the house. Looking out of the office window, I caught sight of two uniformed police officers. *What was going on?* Before I could get downstairs, the uniformed officers had battered down the tenant's door, entered his lounge, gone through to the front door and let in the seventeen plainclothes police thugs. I stood frozen as they burst in, the two uniformed North Wales police officers took charge of the situation, explaining it was a raid and I should come upstairs with them to the lounge.

The three of us sat like three stooges in a bad play in the upstairs lounge, while the other seventeen plainclothes officers rifled through the house. Fifteen from Derby and two from Caernarvon.

"The Derby Police gave us no warning," the older one said, "they just arrived early, and we had no option."

"Why Derby, what's it all about?"

"We don't know Tara, Mick Creedon's their boss."

Creedon the name rang a bell. I had forgotten all about the young detective sergeant in Leicester who was involved in the cover-up of the Westminster pedophile ring. Now my memory was jogged.[70]

---

[70] Judge Sir Richard Henriques who investigated the failure to prosecute Lord Janner concluded that investigating officers Mick Creedon and Kelvyn Ashby were biased against the first alleged victim, a children's home resident, and the case was dropped in 1991. Sir Richard found that the 1991 Leicestershire Police investigation failed to cover basic steps such as checking details of whether a 14-year-old boy, referred to as Complainant 1, had shared hotel rooms with Janner.. Instead police discussed arresting the alleged victim on suspicion of perverting the course of justice despite 10 witnesses supporting his case. http://www.mirror.co.uk/news/uk-news/lord-janner-escaped-child-sex-7208248

"Oh, I remember, he was the investigating officer in the Janner cover-up and the Frank Beck case."

"The Kirkwood Inquiry,"[71] the younger one said.

The memories came tumbling back Detective Sargent Mick Creedon had investigated and arrested Frank Beck, a former children's home manager in Leicester on the 14th of April 1990 just one week before the discovery of supergun. In November 1991, Beck was given the worst sentence short of hanging that any person had ever received in the UK. Five life sentences. At Becks trial, a witness swore on oath that Lord Greville Janner MP had abused him. Beck claimed he was set-up to protect the real abuser Lord Janner. Becks lawyer said he was harassed and persecuted by the Police and had documents stolen. Beck Appealed but a fit man aged 51 he died just weeks before the appeal was heard.

Putting this together with the fact Serial Pedophile Jimmy Saville was told in December 2009 he would not be prosecuted for abusing children at my old school Duncroft Approved School,[72] and the cover-up would continue.[73] Now a couple of weeks later I had a house full of Derby Police under the control of Mick Creedon. Now it all began to drop into place, *'Dam I should have removed the evidence I have about Saville from the loft.'*

---

[71] Janner was given Permission by Inquiry Judge Andrew Kirkwood QC to lie to the press. http://www.mirror.co.uk/news/uk-news/lord-janner-paedophile-inquiry-chief-7689805 Jay Rayner (Journalist) wrote following the arrest of Frank Beck "the establishment, in the shape of his fellow MPs, men such as Labour's Keith Vaz, Tory David Ashby and the then Lib Dem MP now Lord Carlile, closed ranks " to protect Lord Janner QC and deny victims justice.

[72] https://www.theguardian.com/media/2012/oct/24/jimmy-savile-dpp-2009-evidence

[73] On 1st October 2009 Savile was interviewed under caution by Surrey police about four allegations including the Sussex case. But Surrey Police's own review into the investigation said: "Savile was dictating not only where the interview would take place but also who would be present in order to maintain an element of control on his behalf." During the interview Savile threatened the police women that if they pursued the case he would take action. They were intimidated. https://www.theguardian.com/media/2013/jan/11/savile-scandal-missed-chances-prosecute

That evening at around 5.30 the Derby Police left the house, taking with them every single item of value my tenant and I owned. They seized every document in the whole house including my baptism certificate. Their haul included all the evidence concerning arms to Iraq and kickbacks, witness statements from abused children, pages from Dickens dossiers he had given me, the evidence against Sir Leon Brittan QC and Lord Janner QC, Edward Heath amongst numerous others. Years of research and investigation disappeared in a day along with my unfinished manuscript and the thirty-page report into SERCO and Aldermaston.

The detective sergeant from the North Wales Police told me:

"You will not get it back until this is over."

21. NEAT JOB

"Any fool can commit a murder, but it takes an artist to commit a good natural death." Whittaker Chambers

The branches of a mature weeping willow, which had given shelter to a thousand birds, covered me like a bridal veil in drooping leaves. Peeking out from this green and verdant safety, I watched a jet from RAF Valley circle the lake reminding me of giant gray eagle swooping and soaring. *'Was it a coincidence?'*

Banking, with a roar of power the jet disappeared behind the jagged peaks of the Three Sisters Mountains. Peaks struggling towards a sun they could never reach, adorned with stone piles made by countless devotees who had thrown yet another offering on the edifice. In the past, I had carried a stone tribute to heap on the pile of rocks decorating their sacred tops. The land, the mountains and I were one that day.

Scanning the sky's all that remained now was the soft white body of an escaped goose ambling past on the updraft of a minor swirl. Parting the willows falling tendrils, I emerged into the tender warmth of the sun as a summer wind ruffled the stalks of grass at my feet. On the hill behind me, a lonely rabbit stood motionless as a stone.

Under a covering of brown reeds, I could just make out the old wooden boat. With a pull, it slid into view, its old painted surface, long since mottled and distressed with age. Throwing in the oak colored oars, I had carried along the lakes banks, where black toads as countless as the stars had been born and made their way to the water's edge. Stepping in, the swish and thrust of the water sent me tumbling onto the rowing bench. Pushing home the oars into the rowlocks, with a dip and splash I sailed across the sun-dappled water, to the biggest island on the lake. I was no more a creature of the land, but not a creature of the waters I floated like a dream upon the wind carried by the powerful force of my inner being.

It was August. The Swans had vacated the island, taking their brood of squawking signets to the nearby estuary, leaving only a few squabbling Moorhens in occupation. Disembarking, I tapped my breast pocket to confirm the clean and safe to use cell phone was located in its transparent sealed plastic coat. Releasing it, I sat down with a plump where I had landed and dialed.

The line opened but quickly muffled. The only sound was the eek of a hawk circling overhead.

"It's Tara," I said.

Dewi let out his breath, "They've taken-out Gareth."

Flashing into my mind, an image of my old instructor emerged. Alive and vibrant in my thoughts, tall, suited with the worried expression he often wore on his clean-shaven coffee and cream-colored face.

"Why would they take out Gareth he always played 'their' game?"

"No, it's not him, it's Gareth Williams GCHQ."

"What!" I said, shaking my head. "Why for God's sake why?"

"Remember, he had problems with 'the Friends', he didn't come clean to me, but reading it, they tried to set him up with a kid to get a handle on him."

"That's standard practice with that section," I said shivering.

"Now, they've done a neat job on him."

"Very sad news, he was a touch naïve, straight as a dye."

"He saw into the dark eye, Tara and now they've done for him."

Flashing onto the screen of my mind Gareth's billiard ball cropped head with his winning smile appeared. A rush of blood coursed through my temples as my heartbeat quickened, they, had eliminated him.

Moving the phone to my other ear and scanning the horizon, I said, "Scum rises to the top. The black-art pedophiles have taken over."

Gareth Williams decomposing naked body was found that day, jammed into a red-padlocked North Face bag, deposited in his own en-suite bathtub.[74] His Pimlico safe house was State leased but owned by a British Virgin Islands entity named euphemistically New Rodina Limited, which translates to New Homeland in Russian. Purchased with a mortgage from the Royal Bank of Scotland (RBS) a global money-laundering bank bailed out in 2008 by the British Government with an $850 billion dollar bank rescue plan.

His last resting place was a stone's throw from MI6's 'Legoland' Ziggurat HQ and the notorious Dolphin Square, home of spies, politicians, and prostitutes, where children from kids' homes had been trafficked.[75] The squalor of Victorian London remained typified by the bronze dolphin, which cavorted over a pool at the entrance to a place where so many monstrous secrets lurked.

Gulping Dewi said, "He was glad to get away from London to the States, some code he couldn't break. He was a bloody genius of a code breaker and he could hack anything, he hacked into the Kissinger's personal stuff..." he rambled, hard hit by the murder of his friend.

"That was one hell of a risk to take," I said.

"It's the kids, always the kids; he got spooked and wanted out."

Money laundering, organized crime, debt slavery and corruption fitting a well-known pattern. This lay behind the death of a good man, caught up in the lure of a James Bond world, which did not exist,

---

[74] https://www.theguardian.com/world/2010/aug/25/british-spy-dead-in-bath

[75] Kincora child abuse victim trafficked to London to be abused by powerful people. http://www.belfasttelegraph.co.uk/news/northern-ireland/kincora-child-sex-abuse-victim-richard-kerr-i-was-molested-by-powerful-people-at-dolphin-square-and-elm-guest-house-in-london-31121971.html

except in fantasy. Gareth had found it impossible to adapt to the sociopathic lifestyle of deception and fast cars.

They did not consider letting a good man return to obscurity. No that is not how the narcissists, on either side of the pond, play the game.

"Retirement's never been an option," I said. "How did it go down?"

"Suicided, a sex game gone wrong, neat job," he said with the finality of an epitaph.

"And in a safe…, safe-house," his voice carrying the telltale gap of unshed tears.

The rules had changed, if they authorized a job in a safe house.

Bizarre death, a sex game gone wrong is a trademark of a group of State assassins, but any clues were withheld from the Coroner's inquest. William Hague MP, an orchestrator of the child abuse cover-up in North Wales when he was Welsh Secretary, was to sign a Public Interest Immunity Certificate[76], preventing details of Gareth's work becoming public.[77]

In the weeks that followed his murder, attempts were made to discredit and smear Gareth,[78] methods plucked from the same book as used in other intelligence-related deaths such as Milligan's and Rushbridger's.

Stephen Milligan MP. Author, Journalist and PPS to Jonathan Aitken MP was found in Feb 1994 tied to a chair with a necktie of

---

[76] http://publicinterest.info/?q=public-interest-immunity

[77] http://www.dailymail.co.uk/news/article-2126680/Hague-orders-body-bag-spy-evidence-heard-secret-MI6-agents-work-U-S-reported.html

[78] Gareth Williams family furious at sex slurs about their murdered relative. http://www.mirror.co.uk/news/uk-news/spy-death-family-fury-at-lurid-244106.amp

electrical wire, dressed in women's underwear. A Satsuma was shoved into his mouth then as a final insult a black bin liner was thrust over his head.[79] Milligan, like fellow Times Journalist Kim Philby, had also worked for MI6. The Police said it was suicide and the coroner cunningly agreed.

Milligan's boss, Defence Procurement Minister, MI6 agent and former Journalist Jonathan Aitken was head of La Cercle a CIA, Ford Foundation and Rothschild funded black international Intelligence group. Aitken had signed a gag order, in the Matrix Churchill, Arms to Iraq, trial, which would have seen innocent men jailed to cover-up the States dirty secrets.[80]

"Gareth's death is a warning to us," I said. "They took all the documents, my manuscript, computers, hard drives, pen drives, everything."

"They always take the docs," he said, "and writers are the worst, Rusbridger, Webb[81] and Moyal."

Nine days after the death of Milligan, James Rusbridger insider and author of books on Intelligence,[82] died in similarly bizarre circumstances. At the time of his demise, James was looking-into Milligan's death while also working on a controversial book on sex and pornography featuring the Royal Family. An excellent researcher with

---

[79]   https://www.theguardian.com/politics/1994/feb/08/obituaries.stephenbates

[80]   In 1999 Aitken finally fell on his sword of truth and was jailed for perjury. https://www.theguardian.com/politics/1999/jun/08/uk

[81]   http://www.telegraph.co.uk/culture/film/11485819/kill-messenger-gary-webb-true-story.html

[82]   Books by James Rusbridger. The Intelligence Game: The Illusions and Delusions of International Espionage (1989, The Bodley Head, London; also 1992, New Amsterdam) ISBN 0-370-31242-2.Death of a Corsair (1991, Random House).Rusbridger, James, and Nave, Eric Betrayal at Pearl Harbor: how Churchill lured Roosevelt into War (1991, O'Mara, London) ISBN 1-85479-162-1. (1991). Who Sank the "Surcouf"?: The Truth About the Disappearance of the Pride of the French Navy. Ebury Press. ISBN 0-7126-3975-6. His unfinished work was a controversial book around pornography featuring the Royal Family and without doubt child abuse.

inside information he had or would have stumbled upon the Royal

confident prolific pedophile, procurer of children for the rich, Sir Jimmy Savile. The work was unfinished when he suddenly died.

His body hung suspended from two ropes, dressed in a green NCB protective suit (nuclear-biological-chemical) with a raincoat thrown over the top. Wearing a gas mask and rubber gloves and bound with ropes around his ankles, knees and upper thighs, surrounded by scattered photographs and magazines of sexual bondage.[83]

"They'll go for suicide or accident," Dewi said, with a catch in his voice. "He was a good man."

I understood bereavement. I had felt that sharp knife in the heart when my mother died. Seen all reason disappear, leaving just the lonely howl of the wolf take its place.

"Awful for his family. They'll close the book and discredit him for sure."

"They're tying up loose ends, you, Gareth, where will it end. We're all rabbits now." He said.

Dewi was referring to psyops a targeting process where the target is placed in a complex maze of psychological warfare creating a constant negative environment. The victim cannot escape and has nowhere to turn, with Police, Courts, military, medical facilities all subverted to serve them. The State frequently uses plausible deniability, outside contractors composed of ex-intelligence, security and police personnel to terrorize their victims.[84]

---

[83] http://www.independent.co.uk/news/uk/home-news/death-of-an-iconoclast-cal-mccrystal-considers-the-life-of-james-rusbridger-whom-he-met-in-1992-1395357.html

[84] Hall John Dr, Guinea Pigs, 2014 Publisher: Strategic Book Publishing & Rights Agency, LLC, ISBN-10: 163135552X, ISBN-13: 978-1631355523. Dr John Hall a medical doctor from Texas involved in helping targeted victims said: "Over the last decade I have consulted with thousands of people in the United States complaining of exposure and experimentation with electromagnetic weapons technologies..." Dr. Hall believes "based upon former and current publically

The target is subjected to deep capture harassment, which can include:-

Telephone taps with or without remote activation,
Surveillance overt and covert by humans, electronic and satellite,
Threats to themselves, their families, friends and pets,
Financial deprivation and or ruin,
Intimidation,
Electronic interference,
Poisoning often with experimental drugs,
Arrests, persecution,
Thefts of small things,
Discrediting process slander and rumor campaigns,
Cyber Stalking,
Incarceration in mental hospitals,
Scare tactics and occult targeting,
Abduction,
Chipping,
Rape,

The Russians are also experts in psycho warfare and development of the weapons.[85]

"We can't win on their turf," I said, "unless someone steps in to save us."

"They rape and murder children, Tara, what hope do we have?" he sobbed.

Once the State chooses a target, their victim's world becomes dark and terrifying as the State steamrolls over them. The weak, painfully aware they cannot win against the State with all its resources, often take

---

released government research documents as well as victims complaints of torture, that this technology is being used in a non-consensual manner on the global public."

[85] National Security Agency (NSA) insider John St Clair Akwei, in his civil action against the NSA described the "frequencies used by the NSA and other intelligence agencies to access and influence the human body and nervous system." The West in not alone in developing these weapons against their citizens, in 2012 the Russians admitted they were funding development of weapons that will attack the human central nervous system.

their own lives or grow old looking out through the crisscross bars of a mental ward window. The strong fight on struggling with their previous faith in the system until the constant negative environment wears them down. Impoverished, taunted and tormented. Victims may end up hospitalized as insane, or put through the mincing machine of the justice system and jailed.

"They're not just amoral they're evil bastards," he said

The hopelessness of our situation struck us both with the force of sheet lightning. They got their jollies from tormenting us and making us destitute. Against the power of such evil madness, we must bend like the willow in the wind.

"They have long since sold their souls, and we're top of their loose end list because they fear us," I said.

Targeting intelligence insiders often necessitates accelerating the process. Accidents, suicided to order, or a gun to the head. The danger we were now in was as real and as startling as sudden immersion in an ice-cold river with your head held under.

"Are we now more of a danger to our own side?" Dewi postulated. "They just grow stronger."

"They do," I said, "they've subverted the whole system to cover-up their crimes, to take me down; they got pedophile protector Mick Creedon to do their dirty work."

"Yes, the bastard covered up for Janner and the rest of them." His anger like tiny barbs came through the ether.

"But we're in for the long game Dewi."

Catching a movement on the shoreline, maybe a fox or a bunny, but the universe was indicating it was time to go.

"Dewi I have to go," I said.

"Ok, just watch your back."

"Keep the faith; keep aware, I will call again soon when it's safe," I said, ending the call.

Troubled, I stared over the calm green surface of the lake, to the path, which would take me back to Llanfair PG. Lanfairpwllgwyngyllgogerychwyrndrobwllllantysiliogogogoch is the longest place name in the world and my land had long been sacred to the Druids. Anglesey is an island off the west coast of Wales, a green emerald in a sea of gray and blue. Connected to the mainland by a suspension bridge straddling gracefully from landfall to landfall like the two legs of a giant metal Heron.

Gareth's parents lived on the island, and it was here I had last seen their murdered child. A shiver of ice ran through me, then the memory emerged, of wise Druids in flowing white robes with auras of golden rain.

The rhesus negative blood flowing through my veins held the clear memory of my roots, all else had fallen into forgetfulness. My ancestors walked with me again for a moment as I intoned a prayer with them in a tongue lost to the sands and time. Just, over there, behind the copse of white Poplars, Roman invaders had burned the ancient and holy Oak Grove massacring its last five hundred Druid keepers. As they fell one by one to the Roman short sword, the hopes of a free and magnificent people fell with them. Our culture of tolerance, respect for the land and nature, equality of women and the right of each community member, washed away with their blood. Roman law and its elitist system brought slavery to a free people and endless suffering to the world. Gareth Williams had now fallen, sacrificed like his forebears to that same system.

This was all too personal. It was not a game, not a play of the dice. The tumbling ivory whites with the black dots was my life. Every photograph, mother's worn old wedding ring, my baptism certificate, the unfinished draft manuscript gone into some dark Police and MI5 pit. Like any cumbersome multi-national, the greater Intelligence community is riven with schism and the problems of shit always rising to the top.

Just a few months before, the Derby and North Wales Police like an army of soldier ants had raided my home and eaten everything to the bone leaving me but a ghost of life. Now the same devouring system had snuffed out Gareth's life.

22. WRITTEN IN BLOOD

"They lied about WMDs in Iraq, they lied about 911, they lied about the collapse of the economy and made us, the public, foot the bill, they lie and continue to lie about immigration, they lied about the death of Diana, they lied about the death of David Kelly, they lied about their own expenses, they lied about the War on Terror, they lied and continue to lie about drug money in Afghanistan, which is laundered through the international banking system." Unknown.

The writing was on the wall. Written in the blood of agents who had been suicided, jailed, or assassinated. Gareth Williams terrible death was intended as a warning. It was not a warning I could afford to ignore.

Arrested as the mastermind of a multi-million-pound fraud, I knew nothing about; the Crown continued to renew my bail month after torturous month. The Police were using Gang Stalking tactics which they had perfected running police spies. Enlisting the help of two Derby blogger types, the Derby Police fed them restricted information. Repeatedly, they told them my bail would be renewed before they informed me. Encouraged by the Police, the google bloggers increased their vitriol and stalking, so I began a libel action against them and Google. Then I complained to the North Wales Police who sent round, an MI5 run police officer I knew as Andy.

"Nothing we can do while you have a libel action against them and Google," Andy said, sitting on the old sofa in the small apartment. "But give me the evidence, and I will keep it on file."

Handing him copies of their blog articles he took them, speed-reading as he flicked through the pages. The articles confirmed that I was the mastermind of the multi-million-pound fraud and went on to say I sold nuclear weapons with David Cameron.

Andy looked around my humble apartment.

"You must be paying your gang too much Tara," he said, laughing.

"Oh, the ridiculousness of it appeals to their black humor," I replied. "It certainly gave Judge Burgess an excuse to restrain all my assets and steal my money."

Judge Burgess the recorder of Derby had restrained everything I owned, then gone even further and made it illegal for me to spend any money at all save for state benefits which of course he knew I did not have. If I went into a shop and purchased a loaf of bread, I risked arrest and jail for contempt of court.

"But I do not find all this that funny Andy."

"Oh, you're not meant to I'm sure," he smiled.

Eighteen months after my arrest, the State, which had issued to me false passports for as long as I could remember, charged me with stealing my own passport, because my birth date had a six where a zero should have been. It was one of their little jokes. Later they added further ridiculous charges.

The Judge allocated to oversee the case and ensure I received a fair trial was His Honor Judge Nic Parry.

Seven weeks after the raid on my house, Nic Parry[86], a solicitor and a BBC Sports presenter was made into a Crown Court Judge.

Parry had served the secret State by representing notorious pedophile Stephen Norris, at the Waterhouse Inquiry, while I, a

---

[86] Nic Parry is a commentator on Welsh football on BBC in English and S4C in Welsh. He is the regular presenter of the Welsh language football programme Sgorio. He also hosts the sports quiz for young people,PenCampau. http://news.bbc.co.uk/2/hi/uk_news/wales/8541941.stm

trained health advocate, represented my clients who were his client's victims. Parry made a statement to his employers the BBC:

"Our concern at the start of this major inquiry is that perhaps public opinion has swayed the balance far too greatly in favor of those who make allegations of abuse and the understandable anxiety to look after their needs and care may outweigh justice."[87]

My clients viewed Nic Parry with more than a little suspicion. They told me members of the legal professions in North Wales abused them.

In, sensitive, cases the Crown Prosecution Service always hires the best performers, those who they consider a safe pair of hands. The Prosecutor the Crown chose was Barrister Felicity Gerry, who claimed to be an expert on sex crimes. Gerry loved to get on radio and TV, make podcasts and write for magazines.

Six months before she was assigned to my case she had prosecuted and tried to jail the Ratcliff Power Station environmental activists. Her case collapsed when her witness, undercover police officer Mark Kennedy, changed sides.

Mark Kennedy, alias Stone was due to give evidence for the Crown using a false name and identity provided by the Police: but he decided to give up his life of deception and crime and tell the truth.[88] This turn of events meant Gerry had to withdraw hastily and the innocent activists walked free.

Following a spate of headlines about Police spies siring children and having passports and credit cards in the names of dead babies.

---

[87] Nic Parry spoke to the BBC News
http://news.bbc.co.uk/onthisday/hi/dates/stories/january/21/newsid_2506000/2506835.stm

[88] Activists go free after undercover cop changed sides and Prosecutor Felicity Gerry withdraws
https://www.theguardian.com/environment/2011/jan/10/activists-undercover-officer-mark-kennedy

The government did what it always does announce Inquiries. 1) The Undercover policing Inquiry[89], and 2) An Inquiry into the Police use of dead babies Identities to spy on activists[90] For the second Inquiry the Secret State eventually put in charge non-other than, safe pair of hands, Chief Constable Mick Creedon[91], which neatly squares the circle of corruption.

Struggling on against overwhelming odds, I received a call from Colin. He would say nothing over the air but asked to meet at a special place in the Highlands of Scotland. On the drive to Scotland, I was obviously tailed, but that had become so normal to me I hardly bothered.

Arriving at the meeting place, I stood pensively looking out over the sodden moors of Culloden. Here the last hope of a free Scotland had fallen and died in 1745. The moors orange and green tufts of grass transformed before me into running warrior Scots with tartan kilts swinging from their naked waists. Celts, tall and proud charging muskets and cannon with only swords. Magnificent in their bravery but doomed in their cause. The Hanoverian usurper won that day his German line still holding the Crown of Britain.

Like my ancestors before me, I had a thirst for freedom and beauty, which the English Crown could not quench. The Hanoverians like the Hapsburgs sort the destruction of a culture, which even now lay sleeping within my blood and flaming within my heart.

I heard the haunting melody, "…speed bonnie boat like a bird on the wing, over the sea to Skye…" as Colin appeared behind me singing.

"Hello, lass."

"Hello, Colin."

---

[89]   Undercover Policing Inquiry https://www.ucpi.org.uk

[90]   Police stole dead children's identities
https://www.theguardian.com/uk/2013/feb/03/police-spies-identities-dead-children

[91]   Spycops operation Herne Chief Constable Mick Creedon to retire.
http://campaignopposingpolicesurveillance.com/2017/02/02/spycops-investigator-mick-creedon-retires/

"I wanted to meet you here because Tara like our ancestors you cannot win this battle and must flee over the sea."

"Leave my home and land?"

"They will drive you into the ground, they will murder all that is amazing within you, and we cannot stop them."

Taking my hand, he said, "Do not rush to your death like the marvelous warriors whose bones we tread upon here beneath our feet."

I looked down at the earth, feeling the pull of a magic I could not bear.

"But it is my land; my people have lived here for thousands of years, how can I abandon this sacred island?"

"You must save yourself; we will provide what protection we can."

Suddenly the battle of Culloden fought so long ago held a new and personal meaning.

I would drive back home to Wales drinking in the last views of Scotland I would ever see, the lochs, the mountains, the forests and an ineffable power.

During my final days in Britain, I took care not to alert anyone to my flight. The State agents and their media Barrister Felicity Gerry had to believe I was a broken woman. When I finally left my home of twelve years, it had to look as if I had just popped out to the shops and would return at any moment.

The Taxi to take me to the train Station came in the dark of the night. What I dare salvage from my broken life I thrust into a gray suitcase including the small brown teddy named Bernie, whom I had clutched lovingly as a child, Bernie now presided over the dresses, Lowe Alpine mountain gear and a sad assortment of underwear and socks. It was not much for a lifetime of service to a country and people I loved. As I closed the gray lid on the remnants of my life, 'Miss Kitty' jumped on the bed beside it her tortoiseshell face looking up at me, I wept as I put my arms around her. "Miss Kitty, I am sorry darling, I will never be able to hold you again or stroke your head." She snuggled into me, saying goodbye in her own sweet way, "Thank you for your love, Miss Kitty, I only wish I could take you with me, Margaret will feed you."

Margaret lived next door and always looked after Miss Kitty when I went away. She had married a Turkish Intelligence Officer and lived overseas with him for many years. An ardent Welsh nationalist from a family of Welsh Nationalists Margaret amused me with hilarious stories from her youth. Like the time she and her mum found plastic explosives in the house, taken them to the Menai Suspension Bridge and chucked them over the side.

Taking the case, I waited in the dark, by the front door for the Taxi to arrive. The tattered fragments of my life lay like forgotten party streamers in the rain. The colors intermingling red, blue, green, yellow contorted into weird shapes on the floor. Fragments of my life drifted past on the screen behind my eyes vivid shapes taking form, mother's face white hair framing eyes as blue as a speedwell love erupting as an aura around her. The Russian ballet teacher who put me on blocks at three, those tiny pink dancing shoes with the pink ribbons tied around my ankles and I always wanted black ballet pumps.

The Taxi drew up outside, its lights flashing through the big windows. The driver loaded the suitcase into his trunk. Sliding into the back seat of the cab the plastic gave way under my weight. The loss of my home was an open wound. Photos of mother still hung on the walls, the cushion she had embroidered as a gift just before she died lay on the sofa. Memories twirled around my head like visions; I would never step through my front door again.

"Going on holiday?" the taxi driver asked, breaking through the wall of sorrow. I must appear cool.

"Just visiting family," I lied.

He asked the standard questions; I gave the usual answers, aware taxis are often used for intelligence gathering.

In the red computer case lay train tickets to Switzerland in a plastic wallet cozying up to a half drunk bottle of champagne with the stopper pressed firmly on. The champagne made me feel that all was not lost.

St Pancras station is a vast Victorian gothic revival covered area bustling with passengers all going somewhere. The smell of coffee exudes from café's, and you can buy whatever you could need from the open shops. London is a cosmopolitan Metropolis with many races blending in black, brown, coffee, crème, pale and white a juxtaposition of cultures. The ruthless invaders of Celtic lands were almost indistinguishable from those who needed no sword to invade but simply purchased a ticket. Just like the ticket, I had in my bag leading me to seek refuge in a land far from my heritage and birth.

Traversing through the melee, the scents of coffee and the sounds of a thousand feet and voices, I made my way into the Eurostar area. Here I must show my passport to board the train; this was the first and most important hurdle. The girl at the desk hardly glanced at the passport as I went through into the departure lounge.

Sitting on a bench with my back towards a wall I could see the glass entrance doors to my right, the security desk to my left and a glimpse of the platforms behind. Here I waited, anxious to go through the final security and board the train.

On this ordinary bench, I sat watching, my black and white silk skirt and neat heavy black silk mix Jacket was a picture of conformity. I wanted to fit in, with an elegance, which would preclude people from suspecting me.

The glass doors swung open and two armed men strode in. Dressed in black fatigues and carrying their rifles like specialists. However, they were wearing police badges, the British armed police I had met cannot shoot; they closed their eyes when they fired. These two men were professionals; I could tell by their stance, the loving way they cradled their rifles, their nonchalance and presence. They stood guarding the door, watching everyone.

Those who walk in these worlds have a thread of telepathic contact. On subtle levels, these men connected to me and I to them. We knew. *Were they protecting me; or was it a coincidence,*

When the call came, I struggled to my feet, making my way to security. On the wall was a list of items you were not allowed to take on the train.

A thirties something professional in a dark suit was shepherding the passengers, looking at passports and tickets.

As he neared me, I asked, "Is it alright if I take this half-empty bottle of champagne on the train?"

He stopped and grinned, "Of course it is Madam."

Boarding the train, I felt the first wave of relief I was on my way, and I had more friends than I could have hoped for or believed.

In Paris, I had to change stations, which meant buying a ticket for the metro. The subway was buzzing with passengers the sounds of their comings and goings filled the air with urgency. Making my way through the hustle and bustle of a thousand faces, smells and chatter I focused on reaching the correct platform to catch my train to Switzerland.

Without warning a singular clarity and awareness cut through my determination. Behind me two young legionaries rifles slung over their backs followed while in front of me two more cradled uncased rifles with the magazines attached and loaded. They were ready for action, their darting eyes and feral bodies able to spring into action at the drop of a hat.

Despite that, they looked so unbearably young or was it that I was old enough to be their grandmamma. Nevertheless, dangerous situations need young men with lightning fast reactions, clear eyesight and the swagger of not knowing what a perilous world they moved in. I had been that young, that fresh and that unaware.

No one seemed to notice the uncased, rifles with loaded magazines slung over their backs; it would take but a second to bring them up to their shoulders and fire. *Was I in so much danger here in Paris, where I had always considered myself safe?* Having lived in Paris and connected with the French Embassy in Sierra Leone, I spoke a smattering of Parisian French. *What or who were they guarding me against.*

Descending the escalator to the platform below, the two legionaries in front shrunk, so that I was left gazing over their fair young heads, while the two legionaries behind now towered above me. Arriving on the platform for Switzerland the train, with its solid metal smooth edged lines, stood waiting. Checking the carriage number, I swung open the door watching it fall to my left-hand side to reveal two small grid steps. Settling into the seat for the journey to the safety of Switzerland I watched through the window as the young soldiers retreated into the throng of people. Their brown uniforms melting into the colors of coats scarfs and baggage.

23. DIPLOMATIC SOLUTION

"I wish to call on you to join hands in the building of a world in which less people will be forced to flee, and in which refugees are protected until they can safely return home one day." Sadako Ogata

The streets in Bern were broad and clean, every house front tended, crammed and ordinary. Except for the river, which flowed wide and blue with an unremitting passion for the sea. Colors splashed through my eyes, trickling into my mind, vibrant as a trip on LSD. Danger is a drug more potent, more addictive, than any chemical. So with every sense heightened, the thrill of danger forced me on to find an omnipotent power within.

Crossing over the high arched Iron Kirchenfeldbrücke bridge my emotions began to ebb in iridescent whorls with my steps, the scorching sun made the green and red silk dress cling to my legs, the little ruffle of dripping silk at the edge being caught then released between my calves as I walked.

With the bridge behind me, the sun dripped onto the pavements of pale rock as I proceeded onward to the entrance of the Argentinian Embassy. Striding up to the door over soft stones, which had borne silent witness to the feet of visitors, intelligence officers, ambassadors and the occasional cat prowling during the night. Gathering my thoughts back from the cosmos I pushed open the door, reminded that every doorway is a portal into a different world, I stepped through.

Going up to the desk, behind which nondescript young men and women lurked; I fixed attention on a fresh-faced girl in her twenties greeting her with, "Good morning."

"Good-morning, how can I help you?" she replied, a smile lighting up her pretty face.

"I wish to seek asylum in Argentina," I said.

Her welcoming smile dropped as she drank in the coiffured hair, the neat silk dress and the Dolce and Gabbana glasses. I was not Argentina's standard youth asylum seeker from Senegal.

Confronted by her wide-eyed artless incredulity, I repeated, "I wish to seek asylum in Argentina. I am a former British Intelligence agent."

Her eyes grew wide a slight tremble running through her slender body, as her sparkling intelligence took in the importance, the excitement and the possibility of entertainment. In a flow of movement, she passed by the desk, opened the door and came to stand before me.

"Please take a seat," she said, indicating an empty bench, then turned, disappearing through a door on the left.

Perching on the bench the silk of my dress draped over the gray planks transforming its drabness and flowed on to meet the light brown leather of the kitten-heeled open toed-shoes.

Opposite me, three young visitors somber and bleak sat like the proverbial three monkeys silenced by the new tension in the air. Only the faint whispering of my inner voice could be heard in the silent room. The atmosphere was charged with anticipation something unusual was happening. The embassy staffs' normal and boring routine was shattered; shards of their daily illusion lay like scattered confetti. One by one, they emerged from behind the security fence desk to gaze at me for a moment and disappear again. I empathized with their excitement we had all stepped into the movie in which I was the unwitting star with God as the director.

Without warning the door which had swallowed the girl, opened with a swish to frame the Argentinian ambassador Luis Susman. Elegant, suited, carrying his middle years with the skill of a trapeze artist, he welcomed me with a smile, inviting me to pass through the portal.

Luis was well chosen for his ambassadorial role. His handsome, clean-shaven Baileys crème colored face oozed charm and style. Ushering me into his office, I caught a whiff of cinnamon from his jacket. He introduced himself and said, "Please be seated," as he guided me to the crème leather sofa into which I gratefully sank.

"Would you like something to drink?" he said positioning himself opposite me, a light oak coffee table laying informally between us.

"A glass of water would be most welcome, thank you."

He nodded to the young girl, and she left the room.

Our eyes locked his warm brown orbs bored into mine; we understood each other and would be friends. Luis was fascinated to have a British intelligence agent in his office asking for Political Asylum. He was a man to relish the unusual and grasp excitement. Perhaps the fact I was a woman made it even more intriguing.

He asked me what I had worked on and we chatted about arms to Iraq.

"The Malvinas is a top priority. The Labour Government was talking to us about a long-term plan for sovereignty, now the external and internal rhetoric from the Conservative Government is stubborn and inflexible."

Holding a sparkling glass of water the young girl flounced, glided over and placed the glass beside me on the coffee table.

"Thank you," I said as she withdrew.

"Luis, they are inflating the population of the Malvinas, it's all about oil and money," I said.

"Oil!"

"Oil profits for their offshore accounts in innocuous company names based in Panama, Belize, the Caymans, the Seychelles and St Vincent. It's about corporate corruption dressed up as politics. Not about sovereignty."

"We have shared values," he said, smiling at me.

"We do," I agreed.

"The people of Argentina must benefit from the oil reserves in the Malvinas, not corporate entities and politicians taking backhanders," he agreed to reiterate the principle,

"Friends can always come to accord if I can help in some way to work towards a mutually beneficial deal I will."

"Our close relationship with Brazil and the joint development of nuclear weapons means we need to tread carefully when adopting you."

I laughed; as our friendship and mutual respect grew, Luis was candid about Argentina's past and her current position.

Two types of people inhabit our planet, those whose sole consideration is for personal gain: they are detached cruel lovers of money and power, and those who bare compassion and make sacrifices to help other beings. Luis was the second type of person.

"You will not feel strange in Argentina," he said, "it's a country made up of many European immigrants, you will be safe there," he frowned. "But for safety, you must look scruffy."

"Scruffy?"

He pointed to the Rolex watch, a parting gift from a friend who had faltered, "I have nothing else to give you."

Luis commented, "no-one wears a Rolex walking the streets."

Looking in surprise at the innocent, poor man's expensive watch, a parting gift from a well-wisher, "Of course I will follow your advice."

"Once I have spoken to 'people,' I will contact you."

I understood, of course, that although the intelligence personnel at the Embassy would have checked me out 'other people' would have to make decisions.

I gave him the number of my cell phone scrawled on a pad and he handed me his card. A warmth had grown between us and we embraced as he showed me out with genuine friendship.

Back in the hotel room, I tore off the back of the cell phone and replaced the chip. My phone, RFID chip free, had been deactivated for the journey through UK enemy territory and while France was a friend, it was not safe to replace the chip until I was safe in Switzerland. Letting the blackberry renew itself, I lay it down on the crisp royal blue and white bedspread. Not knowing how long I might have to wait, I called room service ordering coffee and sandwiches.

I ate them by the floor length window reclining in the squat leather chair. Before me the plaza lay calm and gray, traversed by the odd person walking with regular steps. Nothing was out of kilter, like a Swiss clock everything was measured.

In the 1300's my Celtic ancestors had walked here fleeing persecution from the King of France, now 700 years later I too had come to the safety of Switzerland. Remnants of my ancestral heritage from the Templars still thrived here in secret. To walk under the long shadow of the Red Cross, following in their footsteps seeking a place of refuge gave me strength. My mother had called us "dragon priests." The intelligence world was one where magic and the harsh real world circled like eagles on a mountain updraft or vultures over a dying man. My Templar blood may be the reason I was still alive.

The dring, dring of the blackberry intruded on my thoughts. "Hello?"

"Look out of your window," the familiar voice told me.

Excited I rushed to look hiding behind the drapes. There Tom was just as I remembered him, a shock of auburn hair glinted in the sun as he emerged from behind a green leaved bush framed the wooden bench in front.

"I see you," I said, to him as he sat down on the bench, his black umbrella held by his knees as if it were a rifle.

Behind him, I spotted a gray-suited man with the build of a rugby player and the square cut jaw of a thug. In an effort at casualness, he tried to blend in with his surroundings; a red riding hood wolf dressed up in a hat and shawl.

"Meet me at 20.00 hrs," he said. "In the restaurant, you walked past today, I will buy you dinner."

"Sounds good."

"Now ditch the phone."

"OK."

Like a magician, he was gone, leaving the rugby player to stand alone on the corner, where the main road rushed into the island plaza. He would stand there for a while.

Waiting at the crossroads another bulky man, whose suit just could not contain his muscles, stood waiting at the traffic lights to cross, but never did. While on the roof opposite I spotted a movement, *were snipers on the roof, looking for snipers on the roofs.*

That evening I made my way through the oldest part of Bern. The narrow roads are cobbled, gray, black, green stones lay touching each other, witnesses to the passage of horse-drawn carriages and carts clopping along, shod hooves causing the pebbles to spark and dank rain firing them into glinting chandeliers.

The soft-heeled shoes made no sound on the ancient pebbles, as I crossed over them to the street of covered arches where Templars once strode. The stones steeped in the heat of a sun that even now sank outside my view made the passageway glow with a warmth, which wafted around me as I ambled through them.

My ancestors walked with me in this old town, which oozed with the power of their presence. They had fled climbing the mountain passes to Switzerland while others sailed to Scotland The Celtic priest line of the Templars held secrets captured from a time before the pyramids were built.

It was the Templars and William Tell, who ended taxation in Switzerland removing power from the Hapsburgs and creating a mountain fastness of neutrality and plenty. But that was before the dark side, the bank of International Settlements in Basel and the bankers took a stranglehold on the planet, creating a sea of debt slaves drowning in their own vulnerability. To walk down these streets of arches was to travel through history, 'veritas vos liberabit – the truth shall set you free'.

Out of the haze of history and warmth the restaurant appeared, tables clung to the pavement under a bright red canvas awning. A tiny haven of peace, which had seen businessmen share plans, families take a meal together and romance blossom as lovers clasped hands across the table falling drunk into each other's eyes.

Stepping past the balustrade, I entered the sanctum. Taking a wooden seat, I sat with my back towards the window facing the arcs of stone with their cobbled front. Hanging above the arches, little metal grates graced rows of windows; a streamer of soft pink blooms escaped a hidden plant pot to dangle in beauty against the starkness of the stone.

The waiter appeared black and white waddling like a happy goose.

"Madam."

"A glass of Champagne please I am waiting for a friend."

"Yes, Madam," he said, waddling back inside.

Somewhere from a room above the tinkle of a young girls laugher dropped down upon me mixing with the pungent smell of fresh coffee.

Glancing down at my watch to check the time I caught the scent of Cartier's Declaration. Raising my eyes, they captured his green eyes looking into mine.

Cut on the bind his dark gray suit hung to perfection a slight silk sheen in the material clasping the fading light. We embraced the warmth of his body was comforting dispelling all the demons lurking in the shadows of my mind I was alone no more. Stepping back, I drank in the flash of his gold watch, the crispness of his ironed white shirt with the little blue stripe, the swing of a gray and blue silk tie knotted to one side covering a coiled spring for a heart just waiting to be triggered into action.

"So what's it like on the wild side?" Tom jibed at me, flopping into the closest chair.

"Every moment is a new beginning."

"Now you have left, the evil empire, you must close the door; your old life is dead."

Like a discarded wedding dress, I felt my old life fall off my shoulders in a heap of lace and silk at my feet. A blue ribbon for luck caught on a breeze flew past me and on to merge with the sky.

"It is not easy to leave everything," I said, "I worked my entire life for my home, mother worked until she was seventy-five leaving me secure as she thought, now it has all been stolen."

He tensed for a fraction of a moment. I sensed the waiter was on his way. Placing a champagne flute next to me with one hand while the other clutched the cardboard menus and a blue leather backed wine list.

"Sir," he said.

"Thank you," Tom said taking the wine list and both menus, he handed me a copy. It was an act of control and dismissal. The waiter hesitated before deciding it did not matter.

Tom turned to me saying, "You would be advised to forget your old home and old life imagine you have been reincarnated."

"Working on it," I replied, "but they even stole my baptism certificate."

"You know the game, it's deliberate, and they wanted to break you," he said.

"They have a manual you know that," he said, "Don't forget the every agents death or imprisonment is pre-planned if required."

"Yes, I remember being told long ago."

"You need to hone your awareness," he said, tapping his right temple with his hand.

"You have become sloppy; remember an agent must know what is coming up ahead. Like an advanced motorist, you must know the terrain, see the signs and master the vehicle of your perception. Only then will you survive. This is a dangerous game... but rejoice you passed the test."

Opening the menu, I scanned the contents. It was relaxing knowing our backs were covered by friendly surveillance lurking in the shadows. Walking in the shadow worlds made you intensely aware of each moment. Every second you knew you were alive and keenly aware of the next avalanche, the next bullet to fly.

As a starter, we ordered the cheese board followed by local smoked Trout served chilled with chopped red onions, capers, basil and crackers with a cilantro yogurt dressing

"Argentina is a great country, and you will get time to go to Antarctica."

He took out a copy similar to the 1531 Oronteus Finaeus map discovered in 1960, laying it on the soft white tablecloth in the corner was stamped with a red cross.

In the hallowed passages of the Templars, we gazed upon the map showing an ice-free Antarctica, mountains and river valleys were shown, now covered with ice for over 5000 years,"

"It's fascinating," I said, tracing the mountains with my index finger.

"Keep the map," he said as the waiter came with plates and cutlery.

"You are following the rat lines," he said, "Nazi's were flown into Buenos Aires by South American Airlines, U boats holed up on the shores, secrets, and boxes saved and unloaded. There are several closed communities there is one you should visit above La Paz in Cordoba, then there is, "Project Ptarmigan…" He paused as the cheese board arrived, homemade bread with white crusted local goat's cheese, soft Brie dripping with age, green apple, melon, red strawberries and light brown-gingered pear chutney.

Eating dinner together as we had done so many times before. Convivial, friendly chatter and laughter about nothing of importance, but keeping that edge always aware.

Back in the hotel room, I shuffled off my clothes, falling into sleep, his last words echoing in my head, "History is a play."

24. SOMEWHERE SAFE

"Refugees are the human dimensions of a failed state." Sam Brownback

The next evening I awoke from a nap to hear the still unfamiliar sound of the cell phone ringing on the bedside table. Shaking away all vestiges of sleep, I picked up the phone.

Luis unmistakable, lilting South American, voice said,

"Come to the Embassy now!"

"Now?" I asked. "What's wrong?"

"Please just come now. It's urgent."

"OK, I will be there as soon as I can get a Taxi."

Making my way outside I caught a cab to the Argentinean Embassy.

Darkness descended over Bern, like a black velvet curtain over a stage, as I knocked on the door. A crack of light appeared as the door opened, a rough man, late twenties, with a small scar on his jawline, looked out through the crack. Without engaging my eyes, he opened the door, ushering me in. Everywhere felt empty as a tomb, the dull thud of my feet echoed around the walls as he showed me to another door, opened it and disappeared.

Inside the darkened room, Luis stood waiting, a worried expression marring his handsome face. His hands trembled as he pushed back the hair from his face in a nervous gesture.

"You must go to Argentina now," he said.

Taking a mental step back, I took in the gravity of the situation. In the silence, I could hear the soft exhalation and inhalation, as his breath labored with the tension.

"What has happened Luis?"

He glanced furtively at the walls: no doubt a hidden ear was listening. For all his expertise as an ambassador, Luis was not used to traveling in the secret and dangerous world of spies.

"You must leave as quickly as possible," he said, ignoring my question.

"OK."

"You will be watched every step of the way," he said. "When you arrive in Buenos Aires wait two weeks for contact."

The palpable fear tumbled around the walls echoed by the pressure of the moment. With a flash of his old suave self, he said

"You 'will' be safe in Argentina I promise, fly as soon as you can for Argentina."

It was clear that no further information would be forthcoming the walls listening ears made that inevitable.

"Thank you, Luis, I understand."

Acceptance of stressful situations and ability to follow instructions was inbuilt into my psyche.

Luis and I walked one final step together towards the embassy door, which would take me out of his life forever; we hugged caught up in the charged atmosphere he whispered: "if you mention this conversation it will be denied, God go with you."

Then I was on the other side of the door. With my heart beating a little too fast.

Back at the hotel, I turned on the computer to look for a flight.

The screen informed me that the next available Delta flight to Argentina was the following morning going via Amsterdam and Atlanta. Waves of doubt tumbled from above cascading through my mind, going back into the European Union (EU) was a dangerous step.

To go to the States I would need an ESTA (US Visa Waiver) form, but an alternative flight did not exist. Therefore, I booked a Delta flight leaving from Geneva and arranged to pick up the tickets at the airport.

Hoisting the cheap silver-gray suitcase onto the bed, I began loading it with what I had salvaged from sixty-two in the UK. It was now all crammed into one poor suitcase.

As expected, the phone rang.

"Hello," Tom said

"Hi, I am to fly ASAP to Argentina, but I have to go through Amsterdam and Atlanta I am not looking forward to that."

"Everything will be OK. We have your back covered."

"But what's happening Luis said I had to go now?"

"We need to get you out," he said, "remember the Foreign Legion in Paris?"

"Yes, I remember."

The young soldiers in the subway two in front of me and two behind in their light brown uniforms with uncased rifles slung over their shoulders. With armed legionnaires two at a time, I had felt as safe as a lion cub with its mum.

"You're picking up tickets in Geneva."

"Yes," I said, "but what about ESTA form I need for the States."

"Don't worry?" he said. "It will come through within the hour."

It did, so I checked out of the hotel in Bern and caught a train to Geneva.

The first leg of my journey began at 7.15 am when I boarded flight HGY77 to Argentina following, as Tom put it, the Nazi ratlines. Once in the air, I had an hour and a half to relax and gather in some energy for the long emotionally charged journey ahead.

Arriving at Schiphol Airport, Amsterdam at nine in the morning I had two hours to wait. Two hours where my enemies could identify and detain me. Disembarking from the plane, I held my emotions in check. I could not afford to let me heart race or sweat to break out. These were all red flags to watchers. I was just another passenger making my way through airport security to board the Delta flight to Atlanta. With the European Arrest Warrant in place, Europe was a dangerous place for me to be.

Propelled along by the mass of passengers moving together like a many-headed beast I did my best to look normal, appear calm and unruffled.

Joining the EU passport queue, I moved into the center of the group of passengers. The drab walls, the smell of humans thrown together, the incessant chatter and bustle of feet and luggage. No one wanted to be here or looked forward to being processed and stamped like sheep. Certainly, I dreaded it.

From a corridor on my right, more and more passengers filtered in. We all now pushed together as one. The space around me disappeared, as the bodies became a throng. We were all backing up in a push towards security and passport control. My heart began to pound. *What was going on?*

A tall woman with smart black wheeled cabin baggage pushed against me.

"Sorry!" she said, with a hint of an Irish accent.

"No problem what a crush."

"Yes it's awful, there's a terrorist alert, so we're all jammed in here like sardines," she said, pulling her wheeled baggage up in front of her to stop it being trampled.

Terrorist alert. Is that good or bad

The disorganized crowd, hands clutching passports and tickets, moved as one beast towards the security desk. As the jammed passenger neared the desk, I could see a frantic man in a white shirt with disheveled hair just waving the jammed passengers.

While two hard-faced, black-suited security men behind watched the melee for their targets. *Were they looking for me?* Then I was at the desk, my heart in my mouth. The security men just looked right over my head as they waved on passengers without even a glance at their passports.

The whole of Schiphol airport was in confusion as I made my way to the departure gate for the flight to Atlanta Georgia. The Islamic terrorist alert meant staff were only looking for young dark-skinned men. *"Thank-you guys";* warmth spread through my body in relief. It was not the first time I had escaped detection because of a terrorist alert. This time I was grateful for the intelligence community's protection. No one was interested in the blond lady in the black and white silk skirt.

Still anxious to get out of Europe, I kept a tight rein on my feelings and an eye out for suspicious people. The full range of travelers hurried back and forth some dragging wheeled carriage baggage behind them; others gazed mesmerized into the shop windows or sat bored perched on uncomfortable plastic seats. Children rolled on the floor or made a bid to escape their parents. The tumble and miasma of airport life oozed like pond slime over my head as I drowned in anxiety to leave Europe behind me.

In what seemed like an eon two girls came to stand behind the boarding desk and began to call out row numbers for boarding. Joining the queue to pass through boarding security. I opened my passport at the photo page and passed through the gateway out of Europe forever.

Walking down the nondescript plastic tube from the airport to the body of the aircraft, I felt another scale of doubt and horror slouch off my back.

There was something warm and friendly about the small Delta aircraft. Buckling the seat belt, I braced myself for the next leg of my escape plan. How many times in my life had I sat belted waiting for a plane to taxi and take off, heart in my mouth, beads of sweat beginning to form on my brow, breath coming a little too fast? Fearing I may be pulled off the plane at the last moment. Time spun again elongating like a rubber band as I waited in breathless anticipation for takeoff. In a moment, the aircraft moved, rolling wheels were jogging over the tarmac. A thrill ran through me as it paused at the head of the runway for the final dash, lumbering like an albatross so ungainly on the land but a picture of gliding beauty in the skies. Here we go the thrill hit my stomach as the plane soared into the air.

Safe now, sailing through the skies I would watch a movie. Taking out the headphones, I fumbled for the console headphone socket. Glancing at the screen my heart lurched, a tortoiseshell cat looked out at me. Silent tears ran down my cheeks splashing onto my hands. The memory of my little cat, whom I had left, but three days ago, threw my emotions into turmoil.

The plane lurched, bringing me back to the present. Miss Kitty's tiny face faded from my mind's eye, as I looked out of the window at the white and gray clouds. Closing my eyes, I drifted into half sleep, waking when lunch arrived in a tinfoil tray with sections of white, brown, gray and lemon. Unappetizing, processed food, which I would never consume, but was so welcome here in the air.

Sleeping again, I dreamed of a big white snake, which curled around the plane to protect me. The Pilot's voice drifted into my dreams.

"We will shortly be landing in Atlanta the temperature is 30 degrees centigrade."

Looking out, I saw the runway lights twinkling below as the plane banked for landing.

Leaving the potted atmosphere of the plane the hot and humid Atlanta air hit me; it was at that moment I knew I had stepped into a world far from the cool green lands of home. Atlanta airport was small with just the odd small aircraft on the runway. Not at all, like the central international hub had I expected.

The passengers from the plane were channeled into the arrival point, from that moment I did not see them again as I was ushered into a line of one. A fresh-faced man in his thirties sat encased in a unit with a computer and equipment. I handed him my passport.

"Put your thumb on the sensor," he said.

I placed my thumb on the dark plate. Turning to this computer, he leaned back in his chair, letting out a slow, steady stream of breath as if something had jumped out of the screen catching him off guard.

"Is there something wrong?" I asked.

He paused, as if not knowing what to reply, "No nothing," he said, "nothing at all. Welcome to the United States."

"But I am in transit for Argentina," I informed him.

He looked straight into my eyes, drew himself up a few inches and said with certainty, "Welcome to the United States Mam."

With that he stamped my passport with an entry stamp handed it back, and I moved on. I had friends in the USA that was good news.

I wandered out into the body of the airport to wait the five slow hours for the flight to Argentina. The small airfield was almost exclusively peopled by US service members, carrying backpacks containing AR 15's, just like my AR sadly left behind in the UK. Desert fatigues were the most dominant dress code, I felt out of place in silks, cashmere and ribbons but no one took any notice.

Passing the smoker's glass cage, I entered a tranquil part of the airport. A complete section of black interlocked metal seats was empty and in semi-darkness. It was perfect. Making my way to the glass panels overlooking the runway I lay down on the floor. Setting my alarm clock for four hours' time, I pummeled the hand luggage into a pillow and closed my eyes.

Sleep was just about to drift over me when I felt a presence. Opening my eyes slyly as cats do, I saw a man in civvies with a long dark coat, who sat bolt upright and immobile eyes focused dead ahead? Like a being from a netherworld, he was watching over me, I could drift off to sleep in safety. I had escaped the parasites, which inhabit the British Isles, once called the 'blessed isles' in the far distant past. *Was it because Britain was a sacred land of light that, dark beings had moved in to destroy its beneficial influence on planet earth.*

The insistent ring of the alarm awakened me. My protector had not moved he sat silently guarding me, from some unknown danger. Standing up, with a cat-like stretch I pushed away the final dregs of sleep. Picked up my baggage nodding to the silent watcher and made my way to the boarding bay for the flight to Buenos Aires.

Stepping out of the airport building and walking across the tarmac to the aircraft the hot night air surrounded me. Walking up the steps and onto the plane *Goodbye Atlanta and thank you*. I was leaving the States without an exit stamp.

Sinking into the window seat, I waited anxiously for takeoff. Time has an awkward way of changing with your feelings; it seemed to take an age for the passengers to settle and the plane to taxi down the runway.

Finally, I was on my way to Argentina following where so many had gone before. A complete Welsh community in 1865, [92] and between 1857 and 1960, more than two million Celts, from Galicia, the Basque Country, Asturias, Cantabria, and Catalonia.[93] On the other hand, there was Reinhardt Gehlen's organization whose agents had shadowed me in Switzerland, they had set up 'rat lines' to ferry Nazi war criminals out of Europe using fake passports.[94]

Sleeping through the dark of the night, I occasionally woke to glimpse the emptiness of the Amazon basin below. Dawn broke while drops of starlight still shimmered in the wake of the jet stream through the skies until the moment darkness turned to crystal droplets shining down onto the clouds below. Each cloud topped with golden threads and painted in crimson flames from the rising sun. Below me lay a new life, a world of contrasts and beauty from the hot jungles of Misiones to the wild passes of the Andes, the rolling pampas down to the towering white crystal castles of glaciers.

The plane landed, and I stepped out to breathe the first gulp of Argentinean air. Mentally, I knelt down to kiss the earth in gratitude for Argentina's protection. It was a chilly day, but even the sterile atmosphere of an airport could not quell the vibrant warmth of the Argentinean people. Their happy spirit touched everything; I was among my people. Collecting my luggage, I ambled through customs without challenge. Making for the safe taxi-ordering desk, I booked a

---

[92] One hundred and forty-seven years before me Welsh Celts sort refuge in Argentina. A community fled Wales settling in the cold, uninhabited wilds of Chubut Patagonia. For 600 years the English had made it illegal to speak the Welsh language. But in Argentina, the closed community spoke Welsh, made Bara Brith, sang welsh songs and held an 'Eisteddfod' every year. And they do so to this day

[93] Argentinians with their roots in Galicia, Catalonia, and the Basque Country have a high percentage of Rh negative blood.

[94] More than 5,000 Nazis were relocated mostly to South and Central America. Nazi's like Klaus Barbie (the butcher of Lyons) helped Latin American governments set up death squads in Chile, Argentina and, El Salvador. This 'help' from Nazi's led to a Military Junta in Argentina and the consequential murder of many political activists and good people.

cab to take me to the city hotel.

Arriving at the Glass fronted doors the cabby carried the one little gray suitcase into the hotel foyer, with Teddy Bernie inside still sleeping. After taking possession of the hotel room and releasing Bernie from his confined space, I rushed downstairs.

The hotel was on Avenue 9 de Julio the widest avenue in the whole world; it teemed with cars, people and coffee shops. It was exciting and comforting, the fear, tension and horror fell away from me. A world of magic, new experiences, tall mountains, tango dancers, Inca shamans lay before me like a fabulous meal arranged on a white tablecloth. But more importantly I was safe and that initially is all a refugee asks.

THE END

About the Author

Andrea Davison is a British born intelligence agent who fled persecution in Britain and now lives in Argentina with her five rescue dogs.

Andrea was involved in scandals spanning the Atlantic, Arms to Iraq, Iran Contra, Lockerbie, terrorism, regime change and the trafficking of children. She was the intelligence advisor to the Labour members of the parliamentary select committee investigating Super-gun. She also worked with Tony Blair MP and other well-known Politicians and journalists.

From an ancient Celtic line, she inherited the 'sight'.

Next book coming soon.

You can find Andrea on Twitter @beforethestars

www.andreadavison.com

APPENDIX

MACUR REVIEW STATEMENT OF ANDREA DAVISON

1.   GENERAL BACKGROUND

The Terms of Reference of the Waterhouse Inquiry announced on 17 June 1996 were:-

(a) To inquire into the abuse of children in care in the former county council areas of Gwynedd and Clwyd since 1974;

(b) To examine whether the agencies and authorities responsible for such care, through the placement of children or through the regulation or management of the facilities, could have prevented the abuse or detected its occurrence at an earlier stage;

(c) To examine the response of the relevant authorities and agencies to allegations and complaints of abuse made either by children in care, children formerly in care or any other persons, excluding scrutiny of whether to prosecute named individuals;

(d) In the light of this examination, to consider whether the relevant caring and investigative agencies discharged their functions appropriately and, in the case of the caring agencies, whether they are doing so now; and to report its findings and make recommendations to the Secretary of State for Wales.

1.1   In 1994 the Jilling's report, by the former Director of Derbyshire Social Services Mr. Jillings and his panel, detailed the rape and torture of children in Care Homes in North Wales.

1.2   The Report stated that allegations involving famous names and paedophile rings were beyond its remit and something best addressed at a potential later public inquiry. It found a child care system in which physical and sexual violence were common, from beatings and bullying to indecent assault and rape. Children who complained of abuse were not believed or were punished for making false allegations.

1.3   Mr. Jillings and his team were hampered by the NWP. The Chief Constable David Owen refused to meet them or help with access to the police major-incident database

1.4   130 boxes of material handed over by the council to the NWP were not made available to the panel, and the council did not allow the inquiry to place a notice in the local press seeking information.

1.5   In November 2012 Roger Dobson for the Independent published:-

The then newly appointed North Wales Chief Constable, who was uncontactable yesterday, refused to meet them or help with access to the police major-incident database. "We were disappointed at the apparent impossibility of obtaining a breakdown of data. We are unable to identify the overall extent of the allegations received by the police in the many witness statements which they took."

1.6   Some one hundred and thirty boxes of material handed over by the council to the police were not made available to the panel, and the Council did not allow the panel to place a notice in the local press seeking information.

1.7   In his report Mr. Jillings said "What we found was horrific and on a significant scale. If the events in children's homes in North Wales were to be translated into a film, Oliver Twist would seem relatively benign. The scale of what happened, and how it was allowed, are a disgrace, and stain on the history of child care in this country."

The significant points are that:-

1.7.1   The North Wales Police (NWP) withheld evidence and obstructed Mr. Jillings. This failure should have been itself the subject of an Inquiry considering the number of NWP Officers named by the victims as abusers. Certainly, Tony Blair who was shadow Home Secretary at that time believed an Outside Force was essential for the truth to be discovered.

1.7.2   The Macur Review could ask the former Chief Constable David Owen to explain his reasons for obstructing Mr. Jillings and make inquiries into the 130 boxes of evidence if these 130 boxes were not provided to the Waterhouse Tribunal. Further inquiry into the reasons why prosecutions did not take place of the NWP Officers named as abusers.

1.7.3   The Council, responsible for using public money to fund Care Homes where children were sexually, physically and mentally abused and who were, responsible for the Care and Protection of the Children therein, obstructed Mr. Jillings by preventing him from advertising for victims to come forward.

1.7.4   in conclusion, the fact that those organisations responsible for the care and protection of the children, and who could alone act on complaints, were actively involved in an apparent cover-up of the rape, sexual abuse, and torture of those children was a matter which should have been properly investigated by an outside Police Force. This was not done. Neither did the Waterhouse Inquiry investigate the vast amount of evidence and testimony of the cover-up or the evidence of an elite paedophile ring.

1.8   Following the public outrage at the suppression of the Jillings report and suffering continued public pressure William Hague, then Secretary of State for Wales was forced in 1996 to order a Tribunal of Inquiry. The Inquiry was to look into allegations of hundreds of cases of child abuse in care homes in former county council areas of Clwyd and Gwynedd between 1974 and 1990. Sir Ronald Waterhouse QC, a retired High Court judge, was appointed to head the inquiry.

1.9   The inquiry began in January 1997 and sat for 203 days, and heard evidence directly from 250 witnesses, attracted 200 additional personal statements, and in total heard from more than 650 people. It cost £13.5 million pounds and produced a report in 2000 called 'Lost in Care' which although damming had limited its scope to mainly abuse inside the homes from the staff. The Inquiry failed to address the allegations of abuse outside of the actual physical curt ledges of Care

Homes which abuse was alleged to be by an elite paedophile network involving allegations against Famous names, Politicians, Police Officers, Judges, Legal Professionals, and Businessmen.

1.10   I intend to demonstrate that in my view the terms of reference of the Waterhouse inquiry were woefully inadequate and where adequate show that the Inquiry restricted its own terms to the extent that it was a very effective Inquiry limited to the abuse and torture by the staff of children in the Care Homes.

1.11   The Result of the limits the Inquiry placed upon itself operated to prevent proper inquiry and investigation into the systematic abuse of children, over decades, and their exploitation by a 'VIP paedophile ring' and use as commodities in the lucrative child porn network with its links to Peter Righton, the Paedophile Information Exchange (PIE) and the Home Office itself. The Inquiry also operated to reduce public speculation into the allegations against public figures and linked criminal activities.

1.12   The resulting report 'Lost in Care' while dealing with the allegations made against staff by the children in effect stifled further investigation into the Elite Paedophile Ring, the child porn Network and the criminal financial gain made by the Directors of the Care Homes and those who procured children for exploitation by an elite Paedophile network.

1.13   Inquires can expose wrongdoing or close down all investigation into the wrongdoing by presenting the fiction that a full investigation has taken place and either the issue has been fully addressed, and nothing outside of those matters discovered exists.

1.14   The current Macur Review has the opportunity to redress the wrongs of the original Inquiry and dispel public concern and concerns of investigators and journalists, whistleblowers and victims that a full and proper investigation will not take place into the historic abuse of children in care. Particularly where that abuse was by public figures, police officers and members of the judiciary.

1.15   The Macur Review should obtain the evidence from all parties who hold evidence and have those accused of abuse or cover-up of the abuse, police, and victims exposed to scrutiny and questioning. This Review has the opportunity to end organised child abuse in the United Kingdom.

2   PERSONAL BACKGROUND IN BRIEF

2.1   During the 80's and 90's I was based in North Wales working for and with the Intelligence Services mainly on investigations concerning the illegal supply of arms and technology to Iraq Iran and the Former Yugoslavia. I was involved in an investigation into the transfer of Chemical and Biological Warfare (CBW) technology to Iraq. At one point I was working with a strictly military intelligence section and when the Gulf war started all the reserves were called up, and I became involved in detecting sabotage and other matters.

2.2   During the course of the investigation clear links were identified between illegal arms sales, drugs trafficking, support for terrorist groups and the sale and distribution of child pornography, including snuff videos. The illegal arms trade is connected to a much larger organised criminal network. The fact that sections of the Conservative Government, the police, and government agencies were involved made it more perilous and destructive to the fabric of society. No-one knew who is working for whom!

2.3   I was later to give evidence of these matters in secret to Lord Justice Scott's Inquiry into 'Arms to Iraq' (Sample Documents 1 and 2)

2.4   I became involved in the investigation of child abuse in 1989 while carrying out a search of a suspect ***** premises. We found hard drugs and child pornography in video and photographic form. Some of it looked ritualistic. The suspect was involved with a company called **** Technology. **** was engaged in research at a building connected with Bangor University. The investigation concerned tech transfer of biological weapons data to Iraq. ******* lived close to and was associated with ****** who ran the ****** gym in ***** following further investigation it was discovered that **** was distributing pornography on a large scale including child porn videos and highly priced snuff videos, where a child would be sexually abused and murdered on film. **** a former mercenary was involved with another mercenary ***** who had been in Angola. ***** were protected by the Police and certain sections of the intelligence community for which they worked, I understand, on contract.

2.5   Following the discovery of the child porn, mentioned above I decided to run an unsanctioned parallel investigation into child pornography. This included an investigation into 'snuff' videos. I discovered some of the children exploited were from local children's homes where there appeared to exist a ready supply of children.

2.6   Having been myself an abused child, cruelly committed at 14years of age to two and a half years in the now infamous Approved School Duncroft; I was keen to expose the abuse of children in state-run establishments. It was at Duncroft that I first learned about the Paedophile Network.

2.7   Around this time I secretly met DC Nick Lewis from the North Wales Drug Squad in a car park in Seiont Manor. I later secretly met Nick Lewis and DI Maldwyn Roberts of a Bridge in Caernarfon at the request of Nick Lewis. They asked me to help them with the an investigation into child abuse and Satanic Ritual Abuse they told me it was a Home Office Directive and asked for my confidence. I agreed to assist them and did so and did share some information with them and passed them evidence. I kept detailed notes in my diary.

2.8   The Macur Review may want to ask DC Nick Lewis and DI Maldwyn Roberts for their testimony concerning these matters.

2.9   When the opportunity arose I asked colleagues to check the Home Office Directive, and they came back with a negative. Following this, I was briefed about PIE, which had at one time been printed in the Home Office and the use of child porn and paedophilia by M15 to control influential people. The briefing included information about the abuse of children in local Care homes, the extended elite paedophile network, and the lucrative child porn sex trade. I was firmly told not to trust anyone in the NWP because they were deeply involved.

2.10   It was at this time I realised the cover-up was actually more revealing than the actual abuse itself and more complex, convoluted and insidious. Without the systematic and organised cover-up of the abuse by the Police, the abuse could not have continued. It became clear to me that the abuse and cover-up was also supported by a network of paedophiles and a wider criminal network involving rogue elements within Police Forces, State Agencies, and Government itself.

2.11   Decades of cover-up had led directly to children being sexually, physically and psychologically abused by protected paedophiles since the 1960's

2.12   The Macur Review has the opportunity to ask the intelligence and security services for all their files, including photographs and videos, on and of politicians and VIPS's involved in paedophile activities and or paedophile rings. Similar files exist on judges, civil servants, and police officers. Some files include police files which have been confiscated by the security services. The intelligence and security services have all the names and details of what happened where and when and who was and is involved. This disclosure is necessary so that those who may have been wrongly accused can be identified. Also, disclosure of this hidden evidence is vital if child abuse, sanctioned, protected and covered-up by state agencies is to be eliminated from the United Kingdom.

2.13   The paedophile network specifically included members of the police and the judiciary as well as businessmen, solicitors, politicians, security, and intelligence insiders. This network by its very nature is linked to other types of organised crime with direct links to the lucrative child porn industry and sex trade, drug trafficking, arms dealing and terrorism. The people involved in these different branches of organised crime covered each other's backs and actively supported each other to their mutual benefit.

2.14   In 1989 the only way to prevent further arms and technology transfer to Iraq was to expose the Governments involvement, and I was instructed to approach the Labour party in opposition and work with the media. Consequently, I worked closely with Politicians in the Labour Party spending much time in Parliament and otherwise I was briefing the Press.

2.15   At the same time I chose to expose child abuse and Police corruption. Working initially with local officials in North Wales including Dennis Parry who was then Labour Leader of Clwyd Council who worked with Malcolm King then head of Clwyd council Social Services children's committee. Dennis Parry said 'we are fighting a machine trying to cover things up.' He accused the NW Police 'of mounting a cover-up to conceal the failure of senior officers and social services executives to reveal the extent of abuse in the children's homes.'

2.16   From 1990 to 1996 I worked with Journalist **** on Scallywag Magazine and its successor Spiked Magazine exposing child abuse. Where details could be verified or affidavits taken from the victims, Scallywag and its successor Spiked published regardless of the consequences. Articles were published about PIE of which Peter Righton and Jimmy Savile were members, and about the Jillings report and Spiked called for a Public Inquiry.

2.17   There was a dedicated group of journalists from HTV, the Independent and Wales On Sunday and freelance journalists such as Eileen Fairweather who from about 1992 started to write and broadcast about the child abuse and the Paedophile Ring.

2.18   The NWP tried to silence me, and I suffered concerted and obvious persecution. Arrested several times and interrogated, the NWP tried to find out who I was working for and repeatedly asked me who I was working for!

2.19   The lady next door to me Mrs Edna Simms disappeared, and I was questioned by Chief Inspector Gareth Luke told me confidently they would find blood and hair in the boot of my vehicle, and he would charge me with her murder. The Police seized my vehicle, documents and other property some of which has never been returned. Months later Mrs Simms was mysteriously found dead. The Macur review has the opportunity to ask retired Chief Inspector Gareth Luke about the death of Mrs Simms and the circumstances surrounding her death.

2.20   While I was assisting the Select committee during the inquiry into 'Arms to Iraq (document 3) and was due to visit Parliament to brief members of the Select Committee I was arrested again and quickly prosecuted for a fraudulent car tax disc on my car. An out of date tax disc had been mysteriously moved from one of my cars to another.

2.21   I visited the Attorney General's office at the request of Sir Patrick Mayhew. I made it clear I was being persecuted by the NWP who were involved with organised crime. I also made it clear that his Government would stop at nothing to cover-up their illegal sales of arms and technology to Iraq and the involvement of Conservative politicians in paedophilia. I made a case that these false arrests were counter-productive as they did nothing to prevent the exposure but in fact made the cover-up more obvious. Following this, all charges was dropped by the Prosecution.

2.22   Due to my prominence in the 'Arms to Iraq' affair, the Conservative Government and those involved in organised crime decided they could not simply silence me. Had this not been the case I am quite certain my life and liberty would have been in serious danger. In fact, I was under close protective surveillance.

2.23   Undaunted by the arrests I continued to liaise with the Press and a growing number of concerned parties who networked. Amongst others, I contacted Geoffrey Dickens MP because of his keen interest in exposing the child porn network and VIP involvement. I also communicated with Tony Blair, who was Shadow Home Secretary at the time, and who was keen to root out and expose Police participation in child abuse and the cover-up of child abuse in North Wales.

2.24   Tony Blair wrote to the then Home Secretary Kenneth Clarke about the child abuse. Kenneth Clarke who was recently Justice Secretary in the current Government dismissed him and indeed anyone who raised concerns about the NWP and child abuse. (Documents 4 and 5)

2.25   Tony Blair later became Prime Minister of the United Kingdom. The Macur Review has the opportunity to invite Tony Blair to disclose what he knew then and subsequently discovered, about NW Police involvement in child abuse. The Review also has the opportunity to invite Tony Blair to disclose what he knew about the cover-up of child abuse and the links to and protection of the elite paedophile ring.

2.26   I campaigned along with Politicians, the Press, and concerned others to have an all reaching Public Inquiry set-up. We sort a Public Inquiry that would investigate the sexual, physical and psychological abuse of children from Care Homes. The abuse was alleged to be by the Directors and staff of the Homes, members of the extended paedophile network which included famous names, police officers, politicians, businessmen and members of the legal profession including judges. We also wanted specifically an investigation into the on-going cover-up and the targeting of investigators, whistle-blowers, and victims.

2.27   Around 1995 I was trained as a mental health advocate and later as an appropriate adult. In my capacity as a Mental Health

Advocate, survivors of the systematic child abuse became my clients. I was in contact with the Waterhouse Inquiry from the very beginning principally on behalf of my clients.

2.28   The Restrictions placed on the Media, by the Waterhouse Inquiry, particularly not to publish names of persons who were named during the Inquiry, unless they had already been convicted, meant that investigation and reporting into the abuse was stifled.

2.29   The resulting publication of the Inquiry report 'Lost in Care was a disappointment because it protected politicians, police officers, and judges. Welsh MP Martyn Jones described the report as "a whitewash" and threatened to use parliamentary privilege to expose protected child abusers. During a debate in parliament, he complained that the report did not name politicians, police officers and judges suspected of abuse during the inquiry.'

2.30   I carefully documented and filed letters and kept contemporaneous notes in reporter's notebooks of interviews with victims and officials and Parliamentarians concerning the child abuse and the cover-up. I kept dairies and all the documents provided to me both openly and in confidence, for example, the contents of the Jillings report and statements from victims. Following the Publication of the Waterhouse Inquiry report 'Lost in Care,' I archived the material collected. Until illness depleted my energy, I continued to investigate child abuse with particular interest in the child porn network and exploitation of children. I collected evidence of, as Eileen Fairweather eloquently puts it, child brothels, transportation routes, hotels and bars, fixers, providers of false documents and outlets for the lucrative trade in images of child abuse.

2.31   Eileen Fairweather an award-winning journalist wrote in November 2012 in the Guardian:-

'Many survivors or those supporting them have tried to point police towards the people and places used to prostitute children. They have identified child brothels, transportation routes, hotels and bars, fixers, providers of false documents and outlets for the lucrative trade in images of child abuse. Almost none of this evidence has ever been acted upon.

The child protection whistleblower who contacted the MP Tom Watson last month did so because he was once in a team of just the kind needed now. I was first in contact with his team and wrote about it 19 years ago before it was abruptly closed down by orders from on high. It was a brilliant prototype, a joint police/social services investigation into the ring around childcare guru Peter Righton. It produced establishment names and revealed an alleged linked cover-up by Labour – let us never forget paedophilia is a cross-party crime – and was shut down as a result. Not one of the implicated men was prosecuted.'

2.32 The Cover-up of Child Abuse is on-going

2.32.1   The majority of my documentary evidence was taken by 19 North Wales and Derby Police Officers headed by DC Winnard and DS Hunt on January 13th, 2010 who emptied my three flats of documents and valuables. The warrant was signed by Derby Judge Burgess. A full list of the thousands of documents taken has never been provided, neither has a list been provided of the thousands of pounds worth of gold jewelry and heirlooms seized at the same time. Save for my tenants firearms, filing cabinet and Rolex watch, over three years later nothing seized has been returned either to me or my tenant who has not even been questioned by the Police. My tenant's solicitors have so far failed to get a response asking for the return of his property and valuables from the NW Police (witness statement available)

2.32.2   I made a concerted effort to get my documents about illegal arms sales and child abuse and journalistic material back, from the Derby and North Wales Police, but whoever was behind the raid on my property had enough power to ignore legitimate requests for the documents return. Clearly, DC Winnard and DS Hunt were not acting on their own as sanction would be required to look at let alone seize/steal and keep documents and computers from a prominent Intelligence Agent and her tenant who held Top Secret clearance and had recently worked in Aldermaston.

2.32.3   In February 2010 Lord Hoyle kindly personally passed a letter to Gordon Brown who was Prime Minister at the time and with whom I had communicated previously. In the letter, I advised Gordon Brown of the seizure of my documents and asked his assistance in getting them returned. (Document 6)

2.32.4   On the 17th March April 2010 Lord Hoyle of Warrington wrote to the Chief Constable of Derby Mike Creedon later to the Chief

Constable of North Wales Mark Polin asking them to return the seized documents and property to my tenant and myself. He asked them for "the return of all documents" (document 7 and 9)

2.32.5   The result was that the Derby Police obtained a Restraint Order from Judge Burgess on the April 7th, 2010 which put a veneer of legitimacy over the Police holding all my property and all my documents, including excluded documents, and prevented anyone asking for their return. To prevent me challenging the Restraint Order, the Court made it a contempt of Court for me to pay for legal advice or assistance. I applied for Legal Aid, but this was refused. This tactic has resulted in not one document or item of property being returned in over three years

2.32.6   Following repeated evidence that the Derby Police were encouraging adverse publicity to be published against me I made a complaint on the 16th of September to Derby Professional Standards complaining that "Almost every document and every moveable item of value was seized from the premises" and "The Seizure not only included a large amount of documents and items not related to the investigation but also included documents subject to legal privilege and excluded material." (A summary of the complaint is included in as Document 10) This, surprisingly, did not elicit the return of the illegally seized material but acts as a record. The trouble with files and evidence on child abuse by prominent people, judges, and police officers is that it invariably disappears.

2.32.7   Judge Nicolas Parry, whom I knew as a solicitor when he represented one or more of the accused paedophiles at the Waterhouse Inquiry eventually presided over my case and still does. Eventually jailing me, in my absence, for a total three years although he admitted no-one had lost any money and no one was harmed. He said I was led into offending by my work for the intelligence services and my fragile mental health. I intend to appeal, this wrongful conviction, as soon as the Court permits me to pay for legal advice and assistance.

2.32.8   The Restraint Order prevented me paying for legal advice or assistance in effect depriving me of adequate legal advice or assistance from the 7th April 2010 until the 30th February 2012 when the Court belatedly granted me Legal Aid. Following this, a further judgment denied me the right to the solicitor of my choice. The Court

Ordered I use Garstangs Solicitors or have no legal help at all. Garstangs refused to follow instructions and were in effect assisting the prosecution either by design or incompetence.

2.32.9 These Court Orders, judgments and restraints prevented me from, and still do prevent me from, obtaining a full list of the documents and property seized from myself and my tenant. This includes not only the documents but thousands of pounds worth of Gold jewelry which along with the documents has been excluded from the selective lists made by the prosecution.

2.32.10 The Macur Review could ask for a full list of the documents seized/taken from my tenant and I and a full list of the valuables seized. So that evidence of child abuse and the cover-up of same can be identified. Together with an explanation as to why proper lists of documents and items seized/taken was not made?

2.32.11 Fortunately some of my diaries, letters and other documents had been saved from the Police raid. A substantial amount of these were stolen, along with my two vehicles, both of which were restrained by a Restraint Order, and other property and my cat, Miss Kitty from North Wales around September 2012.

2.32.12 The thieves Mathew Pike and Robert Ostler, whom I knew as we were once all members of Bangor Gun Club, admitted the theft of my property. They knew that the vehicles were on a Restraint Order and stealing the vehicles or dealing with then while on a Restraint Order made the theft more serious. I made a formal complaint to the NWP and was provided with incident number N207229.

2.32.13 Following this I received an e-mail from one of the thieves Robert Ostler who stole my Land Rover and he wrote to me saying "All of any property Mat may have of yours will be placed in the Land Rover which I have been advised NOT to release to you by Craig Law at RART North Yorkshire" Craig Law of the prosecution appears to have bizarrely authorised the thieves not to return my two vehicles, my property, my documents or my cat.

2.32.14 Would the Macur Review ask Craig Law of RART Yorkshire for a list of the documents stolen so that evidence concerning child abuse and the cover-up can be identified? 2.32.15 Around the 22nd of March 2013 as I was writing this report the prosecution had my Co-operative Bank account into which my State Pension and income is paid frozen. This has left me unable to pay my rent, buy food or medication without which I will rapidly deteriorate and eventually die.

2.32.16   The actions of the Police in wrongfully seizing and withholding evidence of child abuse, and Police treatment of investigators and whistleblowers leads towards a reasonable deduction that; the cover-up of the abuse, particularly in North Wales is continuing and not at all historic.

2.32.17   I believe the reasons behind the perverse actions of the Police and the Prosecuting authorities were to discredit me. They have persecuted my tenant and I, as well as blackmailing witnesses and fabricating evidence. More importantly, their intention could have been to prevent me giving evidence against the paedophile network and linked organised criminal activities, which I had investigated while working for and with the Intelligence Services. Their intention could also have been to seize and conceal evidence of same.

2.32.18   I am currently a refugee in Argentina and the Government have kindly provided entirely free of charge experienced Human Rights lawyers to represent me. My Lawyers have noted and explained to me the clear International Human Rights Abuses perpetrated by the United Kingdom against me and abuse of process.

2.32.19   I am one of many who have been ruthlessly persecuted by those in who fear that the truth about historic and current child abuse will surface. It is likely that the Review will receive testimony of suspicious incidents, arrests, threats and suspicious suicides and accidents.

2.32.20   In November 2012 Wrexham County Councillor Malcolm King had a mysterious accident in which he narrowly escaped death. Cll King, who had recently renewed his campaign for a fresh probe into child abuse in Wales following the revelations about Jimmy Savile, Said "I'm someone who speaks his mind," he said. "If I know something is happening that I don't like I will always speak out and try to change things. "I spent a lot of time when the allegations first surfaced being incredibly paranoid." "I didn't know who to trust other than family. It was a terrible time." Sadly the threats, the intimidation, the arrests and persecution continue.

2.32.21   All this goes to suggest that the cover-up is very much on-going and this puts children at risk. It protects those involved in the child sex trade and allows the persecution of those who are a threat to the paedophiles or a threat to those involved in the historic and current cover-up.

2.32.22   The cover-up should end with the Macur Review so that vulnerable children, now and in the future, can be protected by the agencies of the State. Agencies of the State and their officers and or employees who are involved in child abuse either directly or indirectly should risk prosecution and censure not, as is now the case, immunity, and promotion.

2.32.23   The current Review should be provided with the testimony of those persons who were involved both historically and recently in the destruction and or theft/seizure of evidence concerning child abuse and the cover-up.

2.33   The current review has the opportunity to take testimony from the politicians and journalists and investigators and officials involved

3   **Question 1.** - Were the terms of reference for the Waterhouse Inquiry sufficiently wide to address all matters of legitimate public interest and or disquiet concerning allegations of continuing abuse of children in care and the nature of child care procedures and practice in North Wales?

3.1   The terms of reference were either not far-reaching enough or could be used and were used to restrict the inquiry to areas of investigation. This prevented all matters to which the public had a legitimate interest being examined and or investigated.

3.2   Below is a list identifying the New Child Abuse Inquiries and Police Investigations recently begun by the United Kingdom Government into the decades of Child Abuse and the cover-ups of that abuse;-

a)   Operation Yewtree: Scotland Yard criminal investigation into claims that Jimmy Savile sexually abused young people,

b)   BBC investigation into management failures over the dropping of a Newsnight report into the Savile allegations,

c)   BBC investigation into culture and practices during Sir Jimmy

Savile's career and current policies,

d)   BBC investigation into handling of past sexual harassment claims,

e)   Department of Health investigation into Sir Jimmy Savile's appointment to Broadmoor "taskforce" and his activities at Broadmoor, Stoke Mandeville Hospital, and Leeds General Infirmary,

f)   Director of Public Prosecutions review into decisions not to prosecute Savile in 2009,

g)   North Wales abuse inquiry by National Crime Agency head into abuse claims from 70s and 80s, fresh claims, and police handling of the claims,

h)   Mrs. Justice Macur appointed by PM to review the 2000 Waterhouse review which looked into the north Wales abuse,

i)   Kincora - In March 2013 Police re-opened an investigation into the NI Kincora scandal child abuse scandal PSNI spokesman said: "There is currently a public inquiry on-going in relation to historical abuse. Individuals are being encouraged to contact Judge Hart, who is heading the inquiry."

3.3   Lost in Care was published in 2000, and yet 12 years later a spate of new reviews and investigations have had to be convened because the Waterhouse Inquiry was woefully inadequate and wrongfully avoided exposing the Paedophile ring which Sir Jimmy Savile and others procured for. The Waterhouse inquiry failed to investigate the operation of the elite paedophile ring and the child porn network in North Wales and its links outside of North Wales. It also failed to investigate the cover-up. These failures together with the protection extended to elite paedophiles by the NWP and the CPS aided the paedophiles to not only escape prosecution but to continue to operate.

3.4   I am aware that the following Parliamentarians knew about the elite paedophile ring and the cover-up Willie Whitelaw, John Major, Ken Livingston, Edwina Curry, David Waddington, Michael Howard, Margaret Thatcher, Leon Brittan, Ken Clarke, Tony Blair, Gordon Brown, Geoffrey Dickens, Alun Michael, Rod Richards, John Merek and William Hague.

3.4.1   Ken Livingston said on radio in November 2012:-

"I was raising in parliament against Mrs. Thatcher the Kincora Boys Home where boys were being abused, and MI5 was filming it because they were hoping to be able to blackmail senior politicians in Northern Ireland. They were hoping to catch one of Ian Paisley's MP's - and they never did - and give themselves some leverage. The truth is there's been an awful lot of covering up of paedophiles and paedophile rings for decades and decades."

3.4.2   Tony Blair raised the issue in the early 1990's; as evidenced by the his letters

3.4.3   On the 12th November 1992 Tony Blair wrote to the then Home Secretary Kenneth Clarke:-

"As you will no doubt be aware, the allegations being made against some half a dozen serving and retired police officers in respect of child abuse in North Wales are extremely serious. Assurances have been made by the Deputy Chief Constable of N. Wales that there will be no cover-up in the circumstances can I urge you to consider recommending that an outside police force be involved."

3.4.4   However Kenneth Clarke himself now openly accused of being paedophile by child actor Ben fellows dismissed Tony Blair's concerns and my own.

3.4.5   Rod Richards MP named Sir Peter Morrison as an abuser of children from North Wales care Homes.

3.5   The Macur Review now has the opportunity to ask, for the accused police officers, who remain alive, to be questioned by an outside force. There is also an opportunity to ask Kenneth Clarke why he dismissed the concerns of Tony Blair as well as questioning other politicians as to what they knew and when.

3.6   The Terms of reference restricted the inquiry unnecessarily into abuse from 1974 and to the specific areas of Gwynedd and Clwyd. Complaints have been made that the Organisation owned by and operated under the flag of Bryn Alyn Community included Homes outside of this net such as Cotsbrook Hall in Telford.

3.7   There appears to be no compelling reason not to include all the Care Homes operated by the paedophiles directing the Bryn Alyn Community. This organisation, centered in North Wales was funded by the State and used to procure children for the 'sex trade.'

3.8   Evidence existed that children were removed from the Care Homes in North Wales and Care Homes throughout the United Kingdom where they would be exploited in the sex trade by a sophisticated nationwide organisation of elite paedophiles.

3.9   Allegations were made concerning the exploitation and procurement of children from North Wales Care Homes to a Hotel in Wrexham, Dolphin Square London and private properties in various places which were either owned by paedophiles or were safe-houses owned by various state agencies. The allegations exposed the tip of a network which included Peter Righton, Sir Jimmy Savile and various well-known people in the procurement, exploitation and even murder of children for the sex trade. The public had a legitimate interest in the investigation of these allegations.

3.10   Other allegations while not specifically concerning exploitation of children from care homes in North Wales were made concerning exploitation in other care homes in the UK. The nationwide practice of exploiting children in State care for the sex trade should have been a matter which was taken up by the Waterhouse inquiry or otherwise a recommendation made for a Nationwide Inquiry. Once these allegations of very serious and organised criminal activities surfaced, they should not have been ignored because of the limited terms of reference.

3.11   The Public had a legitimate interest in the full exposure and investigation of the horrific sexual, physical and psychological abuse of children and subsequent and satellite issues arising from that abuse. This included full and proper investigation of public figures, police officers, judges, intelligence personnel, civil servants and others accused of horrific crimes or the cover-up of those crimes. The Public had a legitimate interest in the exposure of the extent and nature of the cover-up and the names and organisation involved in the cover-up. This is particularly the case as more than one Home Secretary was believed to have been involved.

3.12   For there to be no further on-going concern about the welfare of children in North Wales, it was essential to root out, expose and prosecute those who were involved in both the abuse and the cover-up of that abuse.

3.13   Fraud

3.13.1   It is reported that Local authorities paid more than £28 million to the Bryn Alyn community of children's homes. Their owner John Allen was jailed in 1995 for child abuse. John Allen also gave gifts from public funds to the abused children as hush money, one single boy being paid £25,000. The Inquiry, however, did not appear to fully investigate the financial affairs of John Allen or the matter of the gross waste of public money. Public money, which for decades, had been poured into the pockets of paedophiles who were exploiting the children in their care. The Inquiry should have investigated all the people who benefited from this massive fraud and those who covered it up for reasons of personal gain such as the child procurers.

3.14   Suspicious Deaths

3.14.1   Journalist Nick Davies wrote in 1997 that: - On the fringe of the tribunal hearing, there are disturbing suggestions of a violent cover-up. The London Evening Standard has run a series of stories about two brothers, Adrian Johns and Lea Homburg, who were abused by a convicted paedophile named John Allen. Allen ran a complex of homes in North Wales and London and is said to have been supplying boys to wealthy outsiders. The Standard reported that the two brothers were trying to blackmail him when, in April 1992, Adrian was burned to death in a house fire in Brighton. Lea later died in mysterious circumstances.

A dozen others who complained of abuse by the alleged ring have also died. One is said to have slipped on ice on a railway bridge and fallen to his death. Another, who was found dead in his flat was said to have died of natural causes; he was aged 21. Several are said to have committed suicide although, in the case of one of them, his mother said his supposed suicide note was written in someone else's handwriting. Others died apparently through abusing heroin, alcohol, and solvents'.

3.14.2   Suspicious deaths of child abuse victims include:-

a)   Robert Chapman, a former resident of Bryn Alyn, fell to his death from a railway bridge.

b)   Robert Arthur Smith, a former resident of Bryn Alyn, killed himself in May 1978, aged 16, by overdosing on painkillers.

c)   Barry Williams, former resident of Little Acton Assessment center, Clwyd, found dead in a flat where he lived in poverty, aged 21.Peter Davies died 1985.

d)   Adrian Johns, former resident of Bryn Alyn, died in a 1992 fire aged 32 in Brighton, Sussex. Verdict - unlawful killing.

e)   Heath Kelvin Jones, former resident of Bryn Alyn, found dead in 1992 in a bedsit, aged 18. Cause of death, acute respiratory failure due to solvent abuse.

f)   Peter Wynn hanged himself in January 1994, aged 27.

g)   Brendon Randalls, former Bryn Estyn resident, died aged 27 from alcohol abuse in April 1994.

h)   Richard Williams was found dead in a car aged 18 in July 1994.

i)   Craig Wilson hanged himself in November 1994 aged 16.

j)   Lee Johns, also known as Lee Homberg, former resident of Bryn Alyn where it was alleged he had been sexually abused. Died in February 1995 aged 37.

k)   Mark Humphries hanged himself in February 1995 aged 31.

l)   Simon Birley, former resident of Bryn Estyn, was found hanging in May 1995 aged 27

m)   Tony Wallis found dead 1996.

The Macur Review has the opportunity to have these deaths investigated to ascertain if they are indeed part of the cover-up and if there is or is not a sinister reason for the deaths of these men.

3.15   The Waterhouse Inquiry did make some crucial recommendations which still need to be implemented for example Whistle-blowing

3.16   Whistle-blowing

3.16.1   The Inquiry did properly conclude that the discouragement of whistle-blowing may persist and fear of reprisals should be eliminated.

3.16.2   (92) There is real danger that the discouragement of "whistle blowing" may persist and positive action is required to ensure that the new procedures are implemented conscientiously and that any fear of reprisals is eliminated

3.16.3   Whistleblowers continue to be persecuted by those who profit from the exploitation of children. The climate has not improved because those who were active in the cover-up were all left in place, so there was no chance of a culture change.

3.17   Prolific paedophiles like Sir Jimmy Savile who was close to the Royal Family and Margret Thatcher and in and out of Downing Street were positively vetted, Metropolitan Police Commander Peter Spindle said that Savile's crimes were 'vast, predatory and opportunistic' They spanned 54 years ending in 2009 54 years of cover-up."

3.18   The power and influence of the paedophile network in the United Kingdom is such that even Prime Ministers fear to expose it. The abused children were terrified by the power their abusers had over the police and the judiciary "when we were boys it was not just the sex abuse it was the gagging, beatings, and threats to kill which still wake me in the dead of night "recalled one man

3.19   Because the paedophile ring has such far-reaching power, investigators like myself whistleblowers and survivors are at risk of persecution and even assassination. The paedophile ring could silence almost anyone using bribery, blackmail or intimidation or worse. The extent and success of the cover-up provides clear evidence of a powerful, influential, well organised criminal group

3.20   Anne Machon former MI5 officer said: "the need for integrity in intelligence, describing the terrible ethical dilemma that confronts government employees who witness illegal activity including serious threats to public safety and fraud, waste and abuse."

3.21   Cover-up

3.21.1   The Terms of Reference or the interpretation of the Terms of Reference excluded the investigation of Government and its various agencies complicity in the cover-up of child abuse.

3.21.2   While the names of VIP paedophiles are of interest it is, in fact, the cover-up involving the police, Local Government, the security and intelligence services and the Courts which protects paedophiles from exposure and prosecution and enables the persecution of survivors and those who try to expose child abuse

3.21.3   Certainly the public had then and do now have a legitimate interest in learning the extent and nature of the elite paedophile Ring. The public have an even wider interest in the extent of the cover-up and the nature of the agencies involved in the cover-up because this goes to the very heart of the Justice System in the United Kingdom. In this instance the cover-up involved children who were let down by the very system and agencies designed to protect them. The children in effect were without the protection of the United Kingdom because the organs of State had turned against them and were at the very least party to the cover-up if not the actual abuse.

3.21.4   The Guardian - 'True scandal of the child abusers.' June 6, 1996;-

'From East Belfast's Kincora Boys' Home, via Leicestershire, Staffordshire, and London, to the children's homes of Clwyd, we have witnessed 25 years of cover-up. Cover-up, not to protect the innocent but to protect the regularly named elements of the British establishment who surface whenever widespread evidence of child abuse is exposed.

From the public schools right through to the Catholic and Anglican churches, child abuse has been allowed a special place of sanctuary... Social workers, police, security services, local and national political figures remain the common factors in the fall-out from the [child abuse] inquiries...

In case after case, the cycle is described - a child is 'taken into care,' then abused in a home, handed on to an outside paedophile ring and out on to the rent-boy/prostitution circuit beyond, if they live that long... Journalists find themselves battling first with authority, then with the libel laws, to publish the truth about a vast web of abuse.'

4   **Question 2** - Was any undue restriction placed upon the terms of reference to prevent a full inquiry or examination of the evidence in order to protect any individual or organisation?

4.1   I repeat paragraphs:-

3.3 to 3.4.5,

3.8 to 3.9,

3.13 to 3.13.1,

3.17 to 3.18

&

3.21 to 3.21.4.

4.2   The terms of reference were either not far-reaching enough or could be used and were used to restrict the inquiry to areas of investigation which did protect particular Groups and Individuals. Terms of reference are necessary but should have been as wide as possible where the protection of vulnerable children was at issue, and the exploitation of those children by individuals and bodies the State has placed in power over them. Where it was clear those individuals and bodies to whom the State had given control had not just been guilty of wholesale negligence but were accused of exploitation on a grand scale.

4.3   The decision by Sir Ronald Waterhouse, to grant anonymity to all those who are alleged to have belonged to the paedophile ring made it almost impossible for the public to make any judgment about the strength of the allegations.

4.4   Threats by the Sir Ronald Waterhouse of High Court Proceedings for Contempt if journalists or the media mentioned the allegations made during the Inquiry against VIP paedophiles and the ring to which they belonged prevented media exposure of the ring. These threats caused a halt to investigation into the ring.

4.5   The more disturbing effect of protecting elite paedophiles with anonymity was that many victims were afraid to testify against them to the Tribunal. Victims claim that they had been burgled, had their vehicles interfered with and threatened with being murdered or suicided if they talked. For years their complaints of abuse had gone unheard, and they claimed that members of the paedophile ring were protected by the North Wales Police.

4.6   It seems that the Waterhouse Inquiry primarily considered the conduct of the staff at the children's homes and did not look too far beyond this to the wider picture of abuse perpetrated by the paedophile ring operating outside these establishments. A paedophile ring which evidentially included high profile individuals.

4.7   Nick Davies of the Guardian wrote in 1996 that:-

"Policemen, social workers, and prominent public figures have been accused of belonging to a paedophile ring which indulged in a relentless campaign of physical and sexual abuse in children's homes in North Wales. The names of the alleged members of the ring have been given by witnesses in public sessions of the North Wales Child Abuse Tribunal, but they have been suppressed by the tribunal's chairman, Sir Ronald Waterhouse QC, who has threatened the media with High Court proceedings if they print them,"

4.8   Then there are the linked issues of the Paedophile Information Exchange(PIE) and Peter Righton who was a childcare consultant for the National Children's Bureau and then Director of Education at the prestigious National Institute of Social Work in London which had some direct influence over policy matters under the Thatcher government before he lost his reputation when he was convicted in 1992 on charges of importing and distributing illegal pornographic material (for which he was fined £900). The Organisation to which Peter Righton belonged had links to extremely disturbing child abuse, even murder and child pornography including snuff videos. This well-connected organisation had links to the Foreign Office and the Home Office. It was the duty of the tribunal to investigate Peter Righton's and PIE's possible links to the scandal of children abused in care in North Wales."

4.9   Historic Cover-up

4.9.1   What struck me and everyone involved was the extent of the cover-up and the organisations involved in the cover-up. These included the police, the judiciary, the crown prosecution service, hospitals, councils and social services. The crucial organisation involved, fully aware of all the sordid details and without whom the cover-up could not have continued was the NWP

4.9.2   The Terms of Reference or the interpretation of the Terms of Reference excluded the investigation of Government and its various agencies complicity in the cover-up of child abuse. This prevented proper investigation into allegations of child abuse and the subsequent cover-up. People in the following groups were protected.

a)   Senior Politicians,

b)   Legal Professionals including judges,

c)   Businessmen,

d)   Police Officers,

e)   Entertainers,

f)   Paedophile offenders in the wider network, for example, the Peter Righton and Jimmy Savile's network.

4.9.3   Individuals from these groups (Ref 4.9.2 above) named by survivors who were not questioned or investigated about the allegations were certainly protected by the Inquiry. The information about the wider paedophile network and individual paedophiles was not passed on to any other investigating body, as far as I am aware. Certainly, Sir Jimmy Savile would have been apprehended and prosecuted and many children saved if information had been acted upon.

4.9.4   One survivor knowingly wrote that "The people involved in this, are by their very nature secretive, they will never be open and honest about anything they do, and that has, and always will be the case. They lie, cheat, deceive and commit criminal and immoral acts of every kind, as they know full well that they can safely hide behind the facade of respectability that their wealth, power and position brings them."

5   **Question 3** If not, did the Tribunal appear to restrict the terms of reference to avoid investigation or examination of relevant evidence?

5.1   In my opinion, the Tribunal appeared to restrict the terms of reference to avoid investigation or examination of relevant evidence, as I detail in the following paragraphs.

5.2   I repeat paragraphs:-

3.7 to 3.9,

3.11,

3.13.1,

3.14.2,

3.21 to 3.21.4,

4.6

&

4.8.

5.3   The Inquiry did acknowledge there was a paedophile ring operating stating that:-

"(83) During the period under review there was a paedophile ring in the Wrexham and Chester areas in the sense that there were some male persons, many of them known to each other, who were engaged in paedophile activities and were targeting young males in their middle teens. The evidence does not establish that they were solely or mainly interested in persons in care but such youngsters were particularly vulnerable to their approaches."

5.4   Disregarding this they failed to look into it or accept evidence of the paedophile ring or the linked child porn network. Despite the vast illegal profits being made from this particularly heinous organised crime, which operated without restriction centering in North Wales for decades, a proper investigation was not made by the Inquiry and has not been made since.

5.5   Fraud I repeat paragraph 3.13.1

5.6   The decades of sexual, physical and mental abuse of children in the Care Homes and Approved Schools under consideration were not only for the gratification of perverse sexual and sadistic desires of a group of paedophiles but this abuse was also extremely lucrative.

5.7   Large amounts of public funds were paid to paedophiles to run the establishments. All the running costs of maintaining a supply of children available to be sold to VIP paedophiles and available for the making of child pornography was funded by the State.

5.8   Vast profits come from the procurement of children for the child sex trade and lucrative child porn trade. Although the NWP were fully aware of both the abuse and the child sex trade they failed to take proper action to arrest the criminals involved in this sophisticated organised crime or stop the exploitation of societies most vulnerable children.

5.9   Tragically the NWP actually protected elite paedophiles, NWP Officers were named by the survivors of this horrific abuse and not one was charged. Despite the Fact that the paedophile network was identified during the Waterhouse Inquiry and highlighted in the resulting Report 'Lost in Care' the NWP failed to take any action. Lessons certainly were not learned, and those responsible for the

SHOOT THE WOMEN FIRST

cover-up were left in place to infect the system of child care.

5.10   Court Orders destruction of evidence

5.10.1   Damming evidence, in the form of Photographs, of the sexual abuse was ordered by the Court to be destroyed. This protected the paedophiles in the photographs and prevented proper investigation into the paedophile ring.

5.10.2   Sian Griffiths disclosed in November 2012 to the Mirror that:- "Photographs of men abusing boys in the North Wales paedophile scandal were deliberately destroyed by the authorities. Sian Griffiths worked for Clwyd Council in the inquiry office on the 1994 Jillings and six years later on the Waterhouse inquiry which looked into the systematic abuse at the children's homes. She said, "We were supplied with copies of court documents…there was an order made for the book of photos to be destroyed."

The Review has an opportunity to take evidence from Sian Griffiths so as to develop a more comprehensive view of the culture which created a situation where the Court itself ordered the destruction of vital evidence against paedophiles.

5.10.3   Again and again it is revealed that evidence against paedophiles is destroyed or seized and or disappears and is hardly ever apparently recoverable or acted upon.

5.10.4   For example Geoffrey Dickens MP gave a 30-page dossier on child abuse to Home Secretary Leon Brittan in 1983. This has since 'disappeared.' Photographic evidence of child abuse is destroyed by Order of the Court. The Jillings report into child abuse in North Wales was also ordered to be pulped by order of the County Council. Investigators and whistleblowers evidence of child abuse is seized. Evidence of child brothels, transportation routes, hotels and bars, fixers, providers of false documents and outlets for the trade in images of child abuse and snuff videos that has been identified also is ignored. Tragically all the evidence either disappears or is ignored.

Wherever this has happened the Review now has the opportunity to ask those involved to account for the disappearance of evidence of child abuse and reasons why intelligence was and is not acted on.

6   **Question 4** - Was any pressure brought to bear upon those participating in the Inquiry whether as members of the Tribunal, its

staff, legal teams, witnesses or contributors to deflect, deter or conceal evidence of relevance to the Waterhouse Inquiry?

6.1 Pressure was, I understand, brought to bear upon witnesses and pressures of a more nefarious nature existed to prevent exposure of the full facts and evidence concerning child abuse.

6.2 I repeat paragraphs:-

3.17 to 3.19,

4.3 to 4.5,

4.7,

4.9.1 to 4.9.3,

5.3 to 5.4,

&

5.10.2.

6.3 From the information I received from the witnesses

6.3.1 Pressure was brought on them to omit the names of elite paedophiles and restrict their statements to abuse that took place inside the care homes.

6.3.2 Witnesses were discouraged from giving evidence of abuse that took place outside the care homes.

6.4 The above resulted in serious limitations being placed on the witnesses and the evidence they gave, which because of the discouragement did not reflect the extent of the mental, physical and sexual abuse they suffered. It also protected the paedophile ring and the linked criminal organisation.

7 **Question 5** - Were witnesses prevented or discouraged otherwise from giving relevant oral evidence or making statements? If so, by whom and/or in what circumstances.

7.1 I repeat paragraphs 6.3 to 6.4.

7.2 The climate in which witnesses, who did come forward, were expected to give evidence was not conducive to a fair inquiry. Vulnerable witnesses were not offered protection. They had not only suffered years of abuse at the hands of paedophiles but following this many had experienced threats and persecution from the NWP. The State agencies which protected their abusers from prosecution were ever ready to prosecute the vulnerable survivors for misdemeanor's or invented crimes.

7.3   Mr. Jillings former Director of Derbyshire Social Services whose report 'the Jillings report' into the Child abuse in North Wales Children's Homes was pulped on the orders of the Council said he was "baffled by North Wales Police' failure to cooperate with his investigation".

7.4   Although the NWP were aware of both the abuse and the child sex trade they failed to take proper action to arrest the criminals involved in this sophisticated organised crime or stop the exploitation of society's most vulnerable children. Further to this, they protected the VIP elite paedophiles and their own organisation. Nineteen Police officers were named by the survivors of this horrific abuse and not one was properly investigated or charged. There had been a number of failed Police investigations where paedophiles had escaped prosecution and victims had not been listened to.

7.5   Witnesses, I spoke to were aware that VIP paedophiles, which the Inquiry was so clearly protecting from exposure and prosecution, were able to employ means through the police and other agencies to persecute them. It is not too farfetched to say that some were in fear for their lives.

7.6   The Inquiry failed to provide a safe place where witnesses were encouraged to tell the whole truth. It failed to protect the witnesses or offer protection.

7.7   It is vital where decades of cover-up of sexual abuse and mental and physical torture precede an Inquiry that the witnesses are guaranteed a fair hearing and total protection from those who can harm them. This was not done, and in consequence, witnesses were deterred from revealing the whole truth.

7.8   The witnesses had been taken as children by State agencies, in many instances with police involvement and placed in the hands of paedophiles by the State. They were then subjected to years of abuse and torture. If they escaped, the NWP would bring them back to the paedophiles where they would be beaten and placed in solitary confinement.

7.9   This together with the suspicious deaths, interference with vehicles and threats led to a climate of fear where those who would have given evidence were too afraid to do so.

7.10   The Review may consider offering real protection to witnesses and guaranteeing their safety. With protection in place, those who feared to speak out in the Waterhouse Tribunal may feel able to speak out now.

8   **Question 6** - Were all relevant witnesses invited to furnish statements and/or be heard by the Inquiry? If not, why not?

8.1   Relevant witnesses, including journalists, who were involved in the investigation of the sexual, physical and mental abuse of the children in North Wales care homes were not called to give evidence and should have been. Politicians, who knew about the cover-up should have been called but were not. VIP's and a number of police officers who were accused by the victims were not called and should have been.

8.2   I repeat paragraphs:-

3.43.17 to 3.4.53.19,

4.7,

4.8,

4.9.14.9.2,

&

5.10.4.

8.3   Journalist Nick Davies wrote in 1997 that One lawyer who has been involved with the tribunal said he feared that the anonymity ruling was actively discouraging witnesses. "Newspaper readers may well have information of potential value to this tribunal. They may themselves have been the victims of abuse, or they may have worked with the alleged abusers. But if the press is not allowed to inform them of the names of those against whom allegations are made, they will not learn that their information is important. So they will not come forward."

8.4   I had a number of conversations with the inquiry team and found that there was an aura of deep concern and an unwillingness to venture into the dark underbelly of child abuse. It was my opinion that they were ill prepared to explore the truth and may have been actually afraid. Pressure can be brought to bear, and people can be silenced in sophisticated ways.

8.5   It was crucial for the inquiry to investigate the cover-up because without the cover-up the abuse would have been quickly exposed, the abusers arrested and convicted. The cover-up was responsible for permitting the abuse to continue for decades not because the paedophiles were cautious and clever but because the paedophiles could rely on the police, local government, and state agencies to protect them from exposure and prosecution.

8.6   Those who investigated or had intelligence on the cover-up should have been invited to give evidence. Those involved in the cover-up should have been questioned on that specific matter and called to give evidence. But the real cover-up was not mentioned as far as I am aware the inquiry used words like obstruction, incompetence, failure. These are words of excuse; where children were brutally sexually and physically abused over decades because of a deliberate cover-up, excuses are unacceptable.

9   **Question 7** - Were witnesses given adequate support (e.g., legal advice, advocacy or counseling) to facilitate giving evidence to the Inquiry?

9.1   Witnesses were not given adequate support in the form of advocacy or counseling

9.2   The Mental Health advocacy scheme for which I worked one day a week was a private scheme funded by Sainsbury's Plc. We worked mainly with the Hergest unit a mental health unit at Ysybty Gwynedd hospital. We also operated as Appropriate Adults for those vulnerable adults arrested by the NWP. We were not encouraged to support the witnesses to the Inquiry, and no funding was in place. I was the only trained advocate who supported the witnesses from the scheme.

9.3   I had not been trained as a counselor, but I did provide the best service I could. The Survivors went over the abuse with me and in doing so relived the experience. I understand they were promised counselors but as far as I am aware they were not provided.

9.4　　　The victims were dragged into a public court to recite their ordeals and only given expenses if they brought in their bus tickets, so I was told. It was painful to see the trauma they suffered having to relive the terrifying and traumatic experiences without proper support.

9.5　　　The Inquiry was some distance from where my clients lived. All my clients lived in the villages surrounding Bangor. I supported them to the best of my ability and helped with transport on occasion.

9.6　　　My clients were not provided with independent legal advice or representation. A group of 30 or so victims were represented by a Pannone and Partners who are specialists in child abuse Solicitor Richard Scorer from Pannone said in November 2012 that:-

"the terms of reference were an important restriction. It's also fair to say at that time, and were going back to the mid 1990's here at that time the idea that senior public figures, politicians, celebrities could be involved in child abuse was seen as a bit far-fetched." and "We now know of course from recent revelations that it isn't far-fetched at all- and that's part of the reason why it is important that these allegations are looked at again"

9.7　　　The alleged paedophiles had solicitors to represent them. Mold and Caernarfon Crown Court Judge Niclas Parry, then a solicitor, represented one or more of the paedophiles at that time told the BBC at the commencement of the inquiry that:-

"Our concern at the start of this major inquiry is that perhaps public opinion has swayed the balance far too greatly in favor of those who make allegations of abuse and the understandable anxiety to look after their needs and care may outweigh justice."

9.8　　　In my view each vulnerable witness should have been provided with independent legal representation of their choice provided freely by the State. Equality of arms was necessary to prevent bullying and witnesses being told what they could and could not put in their statements. Without proper support, it was highly unlikely vulnerable witnesses felt comfortable in giving evidence or were permitted to give the evidence they would have wished.

9.9　　　I hope the Macur Review will consider providing victims with access to professional counseling and State provided legal advice and assistance on an individual basis. For too long the survivors have been let down by the State which itself was responsible for the horrific abuse they suffered and the legacy of that abuse which has blighted the lives of many.

10   **Question 8** - Were the arrangements made for the Inquiry, including but not limited to, notice of the Inquiry and its proceedings, witness interviewing, location of Tribunal headquarters, configuration of hearing chamber, oral evidence taking, conducive to encourage the participation of relevant witnesses.

10.1   As far as I am aware notice of the inquiry and its proceedings were properly made and reported in the press. However, I was actively involved and following the Inquiries progress. I did not have any clients living outside of the North Wales area.

10.2   I understand from victims that those living outside of North Wales were not informed of the Inquiry or invited to attend. Many Survivors suffer mental difficulties as a direct result of the horrific abuse they suffered, and it should have been obvious they needed to be traced so that they could be encouraged to give evidence. This was not done, and thereby justice was not done.

10.3   For my clients the location was unfortunate and caused them considerable difficulty. This difficulty could have been alleviated if proper arrangements for transport had been made for those witnesses who lived more than 15 miles from the inquiry headquarters especially where witnesses may live in rural areas with poor public transport facilities.

10.4   It is my view that the witnesses were neither adequately supported nor encouraged to attend the Inquiry. Their emotional and mental health was not considered, and it is without doubt that many refused to come forward to give evidence because they did not believe they would have a fair hearing. Others feared the NWP and the power of the monsters who had abused them as children

10.5   For those who did come forward it was traumatic having to relive the terrifying experiences of childhood rape and mental and physical abuse without adequate mental health support.

Had appropriate consideration been given to the witnesses and a proper appreciation of the ordeal they were being asked to go through, then the evidence would have been clearer, and the witnesses would not have suffered further damage.

11   **CONCLUSION**

The Waterhouse team were aware of the allegations of the elite paedophile ring and the cover-up. The existence of an elite paedophile ring has been an open secret in Parliament, the police and security and intelligence services, the courts and local governments for decades. The most compelling necessity to ensure that children were protected in the future was to expose the cover-up, and the Waterhouse Tribunal of Inquiry avoided doing so.

I confirm that the above facts set out in this statement are true to the best of my knowledge and belief.

Andrea Davison

Notes

Notes

Notes

Printed in Great Britain
by Amazon